Diet for Life

Mary Laver's rheumatoid arthritis was first diagnosed when she was twenty-six, recently married, and working as a traffic warden. Shortly afterwards she discovered Dr Dong's diet and soon became convinced of its effectiveness. In view of her remarkable success with the diet Mary was eager to introduce it to other arthritics. After giving many talks and live broadcasts on local radio, as well as press interviews, she realized what enormous public interest there was in a regime which alleviated the painful effects of arthritis. She decided to write a book about it but needed a qualified cook and dietician to work out interesting recipes based on the diet. The person she was seeking needed to be just as committed to the value of the diet as she was.

Three years later she met Margaret Smith, who was a very experienced cook. Margaret had studied catering and institutional management at the Gloucester Training College of Domestic Science. She gained experience in various hotels and catering establishments prior to becoming a Home Service Advisor for the South Western Gas Board. Margaret married an RAF officer and, although family commitments coupled with constant travelling through the Far East, Middle East and Europe curtailed her full-time working life, she still managed to involve herself in adult cookery education and writing articles for magazines. She was even thinking of writing a cookery book when she met Mary Laver and became interested in the Dong Diet.

Dr Dong's diet gave Margaret a theme on which to start writing, and her initial scepticism about the diet's effectiveness was banished when she successfully tried it out on her mother who suffered from osteoarthritis. The relationship between food and the pain of arthritis was clearly demonstrated.

All the recipes in this book have been tried and tested by the authors. It is no secret that the basic diet is very restrictive, and their idea was to make maximum use of what was available in order to create a wide variety of meals for the reader to enjoy whilst still following the diet.

Both authors now live in England. Mary Laver is in Newcastle and Margaret Smith lives near Malmesbury, Wilts. Margaret is a lecturer in the catering department at Chippenham Technical College.

Diet for Life

A Cookbook for Arthritics

Margaret Smith with Mary Laver

foreword by Collin H. Dong, MD
with illustrations by Lola Quaife

Pan Original
Pan Books
London, Sydney and Auckland

First published 1981 by Pan Books Limited

Revised edition published 1993 by PAN BOOKS LIMITED
a division of Pan Macmillan Publishers Limited
Cavaye Place London SW10 9PG
and Basingstoke

Associated companies throughout the world

ISBN 0 330 32721 6

9 8 7 6 5 4 3 2

A CIP catalogue record for this book is available from the British Library

Typeset by Spottiswoode Ballantyne, Colchester, Essex
Printed in England by Cox & Wyman Ltd, Reading, Berkshire

This book is dedicated to all those who suffer from food allergies.

Contents

Acknowledgements

Any reference book stands on a platform created by the work of all those who have previously worked in allied or associated fields relating to the subject-matter. This book is no exception and we would like to acknowledge all the many dieticians, nutritionists and other scientists – too numerous to mention individually – whose work has made the research and the writing of this book possible.

In addition, we would also like to thank all the arthritis sufferers who wrote to us in response to the first edition. Their helpful comments and positive attitude were an inspiration and their encouragement was most welcome.

Our special thanks go to an arthritic lady from Wales. She wrote to say that in the depths of her pain she had finally come to terms with the fact that she was going to be confined to a wheelchair. But as a last resort she bought a copy of the book and tried the diet. She ended her letter by thanking us because she now felt so much better that she had bought herself a bicycle.

Foreword to the First Edition

I have been asked by Mary Laver to write the foreword to this book. After faithfully following the Dong Diet, she recovered from a crippling case of arthritis. A few years ago, the symptoms of another patient of mine, Jane Banks, were also alleviated by employing the diet. Later we collaborated in writing *The Arthritic's Cookbook*, which became a bestseller. In 1975, a second book, *New Hope for the Arthritic*, was written and published. In this book, I explain my hypothesis in detail, and include many case histories. Mrs Banks contributed more recipes. This book has also been universally accepted, as indicated by the hundreds of testimonial letters that I have received from readers in North and South America, Europe, Africa, Australia, and Asia.

The Dong Diet was developed by me years ago when I myself was afflicted with an agonizing case of arthritis. For years my colleagues were unable to treat me successfully with orthodox methods and medications.

I eventually recovered when I eliminated all dairy products, beef, lamb, pork, fruits, spices, alcohol, chemical additives and artificial preservatives from my diet.

In forty-odd years of medical practice I have used the Dong Diet as the basis of treatment for thousands of arthritic patients, with remarkable success. The basic ingredients of my diet consist of fish, chicken, vegetables, rice, potatoes, and plain bread (without additives and preservatives).

My followers claim that they no longer suffer the hardships of arthritis when they adhere to the Dong Diet. I hope that you, too, may benefit from following this diet and that some of the ideas and recipes in this book can inspire you to try it.

Collin H. Dong, MD
July, 1979
San Francisco

Authors' Preface

It's an odd world. We readily accept that nicotine, alcohol and drugs can create havoc with our health and physical well-being; we acknowledge that certain people are allergic to pollen and dust which can cause hay-fever and even more serious respiratory problems; we likewise admit that others are allergic to certain foods – strawberries may give them hives or chocolates bring on migraine. Given all this, is it not strange how we stop short of noting that food allergies may create a condition for diseases such as rheumatoid arthritis to occur?

The aim of this book is two-fold. First, it is intended to provide a diet that is wholesome, nutritious and avoids using those foods which are known to place the arthritis sufferer at risk: in other words, a very basic diet.

Second, in following this diet sufferers are given a starting-point or bench-mark – a basic list of harmless foods upon which they can build and increase their dietary repertoire. Ideally you should stay at this level for six to eight weeks. During this time some relief should be felt and the pain should ease considerably – especially for those who are in the early stages of the disease. After this initial stage, 'prohibited' foods may be introduced experimentally, one at a time. If the symptoms do not recur after a week or so, then fine – you are not allergic to that particular food and may continue to use it. If, however, the pain and symptoms return, then obviously that food item is off limits. As you can see, it is essential to keep a careful record of what you consume.

Incidentally, because the diet is so basic its use is not necessarily limited to arthritic sufferers. If you feel that you could be allergic to certain types of food but are not sure which, then this diet could be just what you need to aid you in your search.

In essence, readers are entering a period of self-assessment, and we wish you all the best on your voyage of discovery and hope. For our part, we trust that our efforts may be instrumental in easing the pain and anguish that conditions such as arthritis can bring. If in so doing we have made what is essentially a very limited diet more interesting, so very much the better.

Margaret Smith
Mary Laver
February 1993

Mary's Story

On 21 October 1974 at my local hospital in Rochester, Kent, my life took a drastic change with these words from the rheumatologist: 'I am afraid, Mrs Laver, it is bad news; you have rheumatoid arthritis.' Then I was left alone, bewildered. The truth now had to be faced, the truth that I had been running away from; there it was, just like a brick wall facing me.

My problems had begun four months earlier when, as a young woman of twenty-six and only two months married, I had started to suffer slight stiffness and pain in my fingers. This did not particularly concern me at the time, even though, three years previously, I had been admitted to the Royal Canadian Hospital, Taplow, for a short period, with suspected arthritis and rheumatic fever. However, as I was visiting my doctor for other reasons, I casually mentioned the condition of my fingers. To my surprise, he appeared rather concerned about these relatively mild symptoms, and arranged for me to see a specialist rheumatologist. Tests and more tests were duly made upon me, while my condition became progressively more painful and affected more and more parts of my anatomy. Finally, the numbing verdict that I had pretended would not come was announced to me, as I have described.

At that moment, the pain and stiffness were not the worst aspects, even though they were bad. No, to me the fear was in the unknown that lay ahead. What help was there? What sort of life was I going to lead? What restrictions would place themselves upon me? Could I still indulge in outdoor activities, like sailing and fell walking? If so, for how long? What were the prospects of having children? Would they inherit arthritis? These, and many other questions, raced through my mind in a blur; I was apprehensive and frightened, and felt as if I was entering a dark tunnel without an exit. Of course, there are individuals and organizations that can answer all those questions, all, that is, except one, which only I could answer; how would I live with the pain and the prospects of a lifetime of arthritis?

My thoughts were suddenly interrupted by the nurse's instructions to wait outside while she obtained a prescription for some pain-killing tablets. You can imagine me sitting there in the large hospital waiting-room on the day set aside for the arthritis specialist. I saw many people, young and old, with arthritis in many forms and many stages, and I listened to their conversations; there was my life laid out before me. Eventually, I left the hospital with a bottle of Orudis tablets and instructions to take three a day. That afternoon I returned to work, but asked for the rest of the day off as I was too upset even to think of doing my job.

I went home and took stock of my disability; I had pain, swelling, and stiffness in my jaw, neck, parts of the spine, shoulders, wrists, hands, hips, knees, ankles and feet. You may notice that I have omitted my elbows; as far as I knew, they were the only joints unaffected.

That evening I happened to be watching a magazine programme on television; one of the persons interviewed was Jane Banks, the American coauthor of a cookery book for arthritics. She talked about how she had suffered from rheumatoid arthritis and visited an American doctor, Dr Collin H. Dong, to whom she had been recommended. He promptly put her on a special diet that he had developed himself, which arrested her complaint and left her free from pain and stiffness; as a result, she and the doctor had written a book together. The interview convinced me that a strict diet might be a possible answer, even though I must admit that it seemed the hard way out of my predicament. Therefore, I started off by searching for other ways of beating my complaint.

I tried hot wax on my hands and feet, drinking a bottle of olive oil a day, visiting an osteopath, wearing a copper bracelet, taking cleansing salts, having hot baths, wearing special undergarments, and experimenting with a variety of potions and lotions. I even tried carrying a nutmeg! In fact, I attempted anything that was suggested that had the slightest chance of working, including 'granny's remedies'. I was clutching at straws, like many arthritics. Some of the methods temporarily and partially alleviated the pain, but most produced no noticeable improvement. I am not condemning all these methods outright, but they just did not work for me.

My pains persisted, especially at night, which deprived me of rest and sleep as I tossed and turned. Sometimes I even retired to the spare room to give my husband an undisturbed night's sleep. Eventually, with my doctor's agreement, I took one more tablet per day to help me sleep. This gave me an extra hour per night, which may not sound much, but was of considerable benefit.

By December of that year my hands had become so swollen that, very reluctantly, I had to have my wedding ring cut off and made four sizes larger. I had already stopped wearing my engagement ring many weeks before. My knees felt as if someone had stuffed cotton wool in the caps. I well remember that one of my biggest problems was getting out of the bath, which took a lot of effort; I spent as much time thinking of how to get out of the bath as I did washing. I never knew there were so many ways of performing this manoeuvre!

One day, while browsing through a local bookshop, I happened to see Dr Dong's cookery book, which had been at the back of my mind since the television programme. I hesitated; what could diet achieve where all the other methods had failed? But I decided to buy the book and investigate further. That evening I discussed the diet and its complications with my husband, and decided that I was going to give it a try. After all, what had I to lose?

Christmas was fast approaching, which is not the easiest time of year to change one's diet. I therefore decided to bias my eating habits towards the diet as best I could until after the festivities. I thought the hardest part would be to cut out milk, but felt it was the best place to start. My tea that evening was milk-free, and did not taste very pleasant. But I very soon found that by not adding sugar, and making the tea weaker (so that I could see the bottom of the cup), it became quite palatable. There was, of course, the problem of my breakfast cereal; water replaced milk, which was not very nice at first, but I soon adjusted to it.

Christmas came and went, and my New Year resolution was to adhere totally to the principles of the diet. I was inspired by one of Dr Dong's many sayings: 'Eating is a habit; all you have to do is change the habit.' This is so true, but so difficult.

To support my resolution, I raided the larder, and out went all foods that were not on the diet, except some of my husband's special favourites. Out of my refrigerator came butter, and in went margarine. In all, I took away as much temptation as I could; drastic situations require drastic measures. It was with my larder sorted out, faith in the diet, sheer determination, and a lot of hope, that I embarked on Dr Dong's diet.

For the first two weeks on the diet there were no obvious signs of improvement, although my body began to feel somehow cleaner. During the third week, while taking a bath, I noticed that the swelling in my knees had subsided, and that I could see my knee-caps for the first time in four months. I was filled with excitement and scepticism.

Gradually, the swelling in my hands and feet subsided; I was able to walk without pain in my hips and, as a bonus, I lost 3 kg (7 lb) in weight to bring me down to a trim 60 kg (9½ st). As the pain eased, I cut down on my tablets, and after five months I stopped taking them altogether. During this period, my employers considered a medical examination necessary because they thought I could not carry out my duties effectively. Fortunately, there was a four-week delay in calling me forward; by the time my medical examination took place, I had been on Dr Dong's diet for six weeks and was feeling much like my old self, but I told the doctor of my previous diagnosis of rheumatoid arthritis. He put me through a series of tests and was surprised at my mobility. He thought that I may have been in a 'recession' and questioned the original diagnosis; he asked for further tests to be taken in three months' time. On the appointed date further tests were made which confirmed my improving condition. He was pleasantly surprised, and saw no reason why I should not continue in my job.

My biggest step was to go back to playing squash after only two months on the diet. My game was not too good, but at least I could move around the court with relative ease. My wedding ring returned to its original size, where it has remained ever since. In fact, life returned completely to normal, and the diet became second nature after about six months of experimentation and adaptation.

During the years that I have been committed to the diet there have been many occasions when I have succumbed to the temptation to deviate from it in small ways, particularly when eating out or with friends. Special sweets and cakes, especially if they have been painstakingly prepared by your hostess, are particularly hard to resist if you have a sweet tooth, as I do. However, when one knows that the resulting pain is only temporary and directly due to these aberrations, the effects become quite tolerable and the dietary diversions may well be worth the consequences. Only the individual can judge what is or is not worthwhile, and the ability to decide soon develops with experience. When eating out, it is often surprisingly easy to stick to the diet by being selective, especially with an à la carte menu. Most of my friends and relations in whose homes I might eat or drink are well aware of my dietary restrictions and enjoy the experience of cooking accordingly; they are certainly not offended if I pick and choose to suit the diet. Close relations, especially, are only too grateful that I have been brought back from the brink of a life of pain and suffering.

What is my husband's attitude to the diet? Having seen the benefits it has brought me, he is only too pleased to join in with it wholeheartedly, although of course he can still enjoy the little extras that are taboo for me. Naturally, he had to acquire some new tastes for certain aspects of the diet, but that was gradually achieved by a combination of his curiosity and the appetizing aromas of the dishes I produced for myself while he was still eating more conventional foods. As a result of the diet, he feels fitter and healthier, and even discovered that he had had an allergy to milk for many years without knowing it.

Inevitably, the biggest impact of the diet on my life has been in enabling me to indulge in the activities I enjoy – and even those I don't, such as the housework! I really appreciate being able to walk, cycle, and go sailing again, instead of just taking them for granted, and I never cease to be amazed at the enjoyment I can now achieve from dancing.

Mary's story: an update

Since this book was first published in 1981 a lot has happened in my life. There have been many shocks and traumas. My husband and I parted and then divorced, resulting in a dramatic change of life-style. As well as taking part in an unsuccessful business venture, I've moved house several times and on one occasion was moving when my beloved father died. All these stressful incidents have inevitably taken their toll by draining me mentally and emotionally and affecting me physically as well.

We need to treat our bodies as a whole, complete entity. Our physical being is so often linked with our mental state. This fact, once recognized by our forefathers but later obscured by modern drugs, now seems to be receiving the attention it truly deserves. The miraculous advances of modern medicine are beginning to reflect these half-remembered truths of yesterday.

The traumatic events and worries of the past few years have left me somewhat worn down and physically disabled compared to the person I was when I first collaborated with Margaret. Now there are times when a wheelchair is my easiest mode of transport. This is because of problems I am having with my knees and right ankle. Not so long ago – May 1988 – I spent some time backpacking around the USA, and it is thought that the heavy rucksack and constant travelling may have damaged the joints and that this, coupled with stress and my ever-present arthritic condition, could have caused the breakdown of certain knee ligaments. At the time of writing I am awaiting the results of an in-depth medical examination. In the meantime I continue to 'listen' to my body and make sure that I rest and eat the foods that are basic to this diet – rice and vegetables. From time to time I have also found relief with massage and acupuncture.

However, the most important point to bear in mind is that I suffer very little pain, and this despite the fact that I am not taking any drugs. Not being dulled by any side-effects, I am fully alert mentally and am currently studying for an Open University degree. I am more than ever convinced that without following the diet I would in no way be able to do what I do now.

We never promised a cure for arthritis; sadly, no one can do that – certainly not at the moment. But we do promise an improved quality of life with less pain and less joint stiffness and swelling. Gradually, with your own doctor's agreement, you too will find less need for drugs or painkillers.

It is interesting to note that The Arthritis and Rheumatism Council is now saying what we have believed for years – that a diet free from animal fat and chemical additives will be a positive advantage and should be tried by all arthritics. Your own doctor should have more literature on this.

I wish you well.

Part I

The Principles of the Diet

Introduction

Margaret:

Over the past ten years we have heard from many arthritics who, after following the principles of the Dong Diet, have experienced easing of their swollen joints and great relief from their pain. The diet has not cured their arthritis, but it has enabled them to lead a fuller and more active life. Mary has never been 'cured' of her arthritis but has still managed to remain pain-free. Although I do not suffer from this illness myself, I am prone to the other scourge that most osteoarthritics suffer from – putting on excess weight! Euphemistically known as 'middle-age spread', this condition should more truthfully be described as 'input greater than expenditure'.

When Mary and I were working on the original manuscript, we shared a house at one point. We tested the recipes jointly and during the two months that we were together my own weight was reduced to the lowest it had been since my twenties and, what is more, I had more energy than usual. So what was the connection? On the Dong Diet my only source of complete protein was chicken, fish and soya products. I ate a greater variety of vegetables with additional bulk from cereal products. Since then, sadly, I have regressed: during the busy times of holding down a full-time lecturing post at a technical college and running a home for my RAF officer husband, I re-introduced cow's milk and ate more meat and whole eggs. Result: my dress size gradually increased. I did not get enormously fat because my background in nutrition training would not allow me to go overboard. What I am talking about is that imperceptible weight increase that robs you of efficiency and slows you down. Your waistband seems a bit tight, so you simply undo it surreptitiously after a big meal. Then the day comes when you have to go and buy a new skirt and swear that the sizes are much skimpier than they used to be! Soon you find yourself having to wear the next size up. Incidentally, I know I am writing from a woman's point of view, but if you are a man, hasn't the same thing happened to you? You go to put on your best suit only to find that it seems to have shrunk around the waistband while it's been hanging in the wardrobe! The major point I am making is that calorie intake in proportion to energy output is a crucial ratio, especially for sufferers like osteoarthritics. As they inevitably become less mobile, they find that they do not have the same energy burn they once had, and the excess intake gets converted into body fat, which in turn decreases their mobility even more. Their weight increases quite quickly and that puts more pressure on their joints, causing yet more pain and consequently reducing their mobility still further. Put simply, they are going to have to diet.

The title of this book, *Diet for Life*, was chosen because it is just what it says it is, A DIET FOR LIFE. I am not talking about the next few weeks or months, but a lifelong commitment. When we talk about diets we usually mean a temporary one which reduces weight to a desired target. A conservative estimate would probably reveal that 50 per cent of all adults, male and female, have tried at least one diet, some doubtless even more. I am no exception and I confess to having tried most of the sensible ones. From time to time I have lost weight, with varying degrees of success, but as the years have gone by I have tended to become less active and the success rate has decreased accordingly. Osteoarthritis is usually diagnosed in more mature people and, although it is not always linked to obesity, excess weight may well be a significant factor. It is here that the Dong Diet is of great benefit. Modern nutritional thinking exhorts us to eat less animal fat, more fresh vegetables and whole-grain cereals, and to eat fewer processed foods. This is what makes the Dong Diet so up-to-date.

And so to the rest of the book. As an arthritic you will probably have tried many drugs and treatments and will be taking advice from your GP. Before you decide to try the revised eating plan we do suggest you talk to your doctor. We have no direct connections with the medical profession and of course do not know you personally, nor are we familiar with any other medical problems you may have. But we can say that the diet is nutritionally sound in that it contains all the essential nutrients you require every day, even though a number of foods are excluded.

If your doctor agrees, try the diet. We are sure you will join the growing number of people who are finding that thinking carefully about what they eat improves their health and proves to be the most useful thing that they can do for themselves. If you have others in your family who are not arthritics, then much of what you prepare for yourself on this diet plan will be of equal benefit to them because it so closely mirrors the information that is currently being constantly broadcast about what people should eat. Of course, they can supplement their intake; they can eat fruit whereas for you it is not a good idea, although Mary admits to having the occasional banana. (However, as a banana needs very little digestion, it is always better to eat it on its own, ideally for breakfast.)

In the pages that follow I have given you a selection of menu plans and ideas to get you started, and I have tried to keep them as simple as possible. As you experience the benefits of following the diet, then you can in turn try the other recipes and add to the variety of your cuisine.

Foods You May/May Not Eat

What you may eat

All vegetables, including avocado pears
Bread, flour to which nothing listed under 'What you may not eat'
has been added
Rice of all kinds: brown, white, wild
Soya bean products
Quorn
Filo pastry
Sunflower seeds
Nuts
Honey
Egg whites
Margarine, free from milk solids
Seafood
Vegetable oils, particularly safflower and corn
Tea
Coffee
Herbal infusions
Soda water
Herbs
Salt
Sugar

What you may eat occasionally

Breast of chicken and chicken stock
A small amount of wine in cooking
A small rye whisky
A small pinch of spicy seasoning such as curry powder
Noodles or spaghetti, since the amount of egg is relatively small and
somewhat broken down in the cooking
Crispbreads without milk solids and additives

What you may not eat

Meat in any form, including stock
Fruit of any kind, including tomatoes
Dairy produce, including egg yolks, milk, cheese, yoghurt
Vinegar, or any other acid
Pepper (definitely)
Chocolate
Dry roasted nuts (the process involves the use of monosodium glutamate)
Alcoholic beverages
Soft drinks (unless without additives)
All additives, preservatives, chemicals, most especially monosodium glutamate. One exception to this rule is the lecithin in margarine.

What you may eat

All vegetables

Vegetables will be forming the backbone of your diet, and by vegetables I do not mean plates of overcooked cabbage or soggy Brussels sprouts. Unfortunately, in Great Britain we are rather careless about the way in which we cook and serve our vegetables. Over- rather than undercooking is more usual, and the vegetables are served as an accompaniment, not very often as a dish on their own. Therefore, for you to get the very best from your vegetables, you may have to readjust a little.

Vegetables are a good source of vitamin C; they also contain small amounts of vitamins E and A, protein and minerals. As well as these nutrients, vegetables contain fibre, usually in the form of cellulose and pectin. The fibre is not a nutrient, because it is not absorbed by the body, but it is vital, as it passes through the digestive tract and is eliminated, thus preventing constipation. The lack of vegetables in a diet is often a contributory factor behind many of today's tummy ailments.

There are lots of vegetables on the market today, more than at any time in the past. The more we travel abroad and try foreign foods, the greater is the demand in the shops for foreign vegetables. Most greengrocers now sell green and red peppers, aubergines, artichokes and courgettes, as well as the more common English vegetables such as broccoli, cabbage, cauliflower, carrots, onions and others.

As there is no fruit in this diet you must look to vegetables to supply your daily requirement of vitamin C. If the vegetables are eaten raw you will receive the maximum amount of vitamin C available since it will not have been destroyed by the cooking process. Indeed raw vegetables, especially when they are crisp, fresh and neatly cut up, can provide a crunchy snack. Every day you will need about 30 milligrams – it may not appear to be a great amount but this is vital for your health and general well-being.

Unfortunately, vitamin C is one of the least stable vitamins, and it can be destroyed very easily. Vegetables have their highest vitamin C content at harvest, and from that moment on it starts to decline. In the kitchen, when the vegetables are prepared, a loss occurs whenever the vegetables are cut. This is because an enzyme is released on the cut surface which oxidizes vitamin C. On one stage more, to the cooking. Vitamin C is water soluble, so it leaks out of the vegetables into the cooking water; the longer they are in the water, the more vitamin C is destroyed. Finally, when the vegetables are drained, and kept warm until served, a further loss can occur, so that vegetables kept hot for more than a few minutes can lose even the little bit of vitamin C that has been left. Canteen vegetables are highly unlikely to contain any vitamin C whatsoever.

Having read all that, I am quite sure you must be wondering how on earth we manage to get any vitamin C at all. In fact, we do usually get enough, but these things must be noted because there is no supplement of vitamin C coming into our diet in fruit, so extra care must be taken.

First, buy your vegetables and use them as fresh as possible. Prepare them just before you want to cook them, and do not cut them up too much. When ready to cook them, plunge them into boiling water, as this kills off the enzyme which destroys the vitamin C on the cut surface. Use a minimum of water, cook for the least amount of time, and use the cooking water immediately for gravy. Vegetable water left hanging around from one meal to the next, is almost useless.

Steaming vegetables or cooking them in a microwave are both very good ways to preserve vitamin C.

Potatoes are a good source of vitamin C. In fact, probably about 25% of each day's supply comes from potatoes alone. The newer the potato, the greater the amount of vitamin C. Salad vegetables are another good source, especially if they are eaten really fresh.

Of course, it would be best to grow your own vegetables, but obviously not everyone can do this. Frozen vegetables are usually very good value; these are frozen within a very short time of harvest, and can often have a higher vitamin C content than vegetables bought in a market. But do make sure that the frozen vegetables are not prepared in a sauce as the sauce may contain ingredients not allowed on the diet. Destruction of vitamin C takes place as the frozen vegetables are left to defrost, so cook them straight from the frozen state, follow the directions on the packet, and only cook for the specified length of time.

Bread and flour

Flour is made by milling grain until a fine powder is formed. The grain is usually wheat, although flour can be ground from other cereals, pulses or nuts. In this context we mean the flour made by milling wheat.

Wheat grains were originally ground between stones, but nowadays steel roller mills are more often used. The resulting flour from either kind of mill is called wholemeal flour because it is made from 100% of the grain. This wholemeal flour is the only flour protected by law from having anything added to it, and it is the purest flour you can buy.

Wholemeal flour, however, is very heavy with bran and, although very suitable for bread-making, it is rather heavy for making cakes and sponges. There is a lighter flour, suitable for Dr Dong's diet, which is an 80% extraction flour. In this case, 20% of the bran and germ are removed resulting in a lighter flour which is more suitable for making cakes than the heavier wholemeal flour. In bread-making you can use one or other of these flours, or you can mix them as you wish to produce the coloured and textured bread you like. There are several recipes for different breads in the recipe section of this book. The 80% flour is suitable for making cakes and although it is not as light as the flours you may have been used to, it is well worth experimenting to produce good cakes; the recipes in Part II of the book will help you.

These two flours, wholemeal and 80% extraction flour, are really the only two pure flours on the market. Wholemeal flour is free from additives such as bleaches and improvers. Any flour milled and sold with more than 20% of its bulk taken away has to have additives. In 1963 regulations were passed which means that to all flour which is sold containing less than 80% of the whole grain, iron, vitamin B_1, nicotinic acid and chalk must be added. This protects the consumer from deficiency, and these additives are completely acceptable for the arthritic. Unfortunately, as far as I have been able to establish, all flours on general sale in supermarkets and grocery stores have other additives as well, usually in the form of improvers and bleaches. These flours are best avoided.

Both wholemeal and 80% wheat flours are obtainable from health food shops, and wholemeal flour can be bought from ordinary supermarkets and grocery stores. But do watch out for the word *wheatmeal*. This is a wholemeal flour, but, unlike the true wholemeal, it is not protected by law, and usually contains additives.

The other commonly used flours, such as soya flour and cornflour, are pure products and any type can be used.

The very best bread for you to use is your own. That way you can choose your flour carefully, and make your bread using only ingredients within the diet. But, sadly, this is not always possible. Bread-making does take time and a fair amount of effort, though if you are fortunate and own a food mixer and a deep freeze, then much of the chore of bread-making can be taken away. A good large batch can be made, and then frozen for use later. For people who find this impossible, bread should be bought from small independent bakers or health food shops. The baker will then be able to tell you exactly what flour he is using. Like wholemeal flour, true wholemeal bread is also protected by law and cannot contain any additives. However, wholemeal bread often gets confused with brown bread or granary bread or other types, and these can contain any permitted additive the baker wishes to use.

Bread-making has changed drastically over the past few years. It is said that the consumer wants a standard loaf, cut and wrapped, which does not go stale quickly and is uniform in texture, and so this is what is made in vast quantities by the large national bakeries. Such bread is not made in the traditional way, in which the dough is left to prove twice, once after mixing and again before baking. This bread is made by a process known as the Chorley Wood Process. High-powered machinery is used, and improvers are added to the weak British flours with the result that there is no need to prove the dough at all. A uniform spongy bread which cuts and stores well is the result. There are other methods used today in the baking industry, but they all need additives to make the standard loaf. For a list of these additives see the section about Bread in the chapter on food additives.

Mention has been made of 'weak' British flour. Essentially there are two types of flour, 'weak' and 'strong'. The word 'strong' refers to the flour's gluten content. The higher the gluten content of the flour, the lighter the resulting bread, because the gluten (which is the protein in the flour) traps air within the bread dough. This is how it happens: gluten is an elastic substance which stretches and becomes more elastic as the dough is kneaded; as the gluten stretches it traps air bubbles within the fibre of the flour. When the bread is cooked the air, plus the carbon dioxide produced by the yeast, expands, thus forcing apart the gluten and fibre, and because they are 'strong' they stay apart and harden during the cooking process. The result is a crisp crust enclosing lots of little air bubbles trapped within the fibres of the bread. British wheat has a low gluten content which means that if traditional bread-making methods are used a bread with a very heavy texture is produced. Hence the preference for strong imported wheats when making home baked bread. However, imported wheats cost so much more than British wheat, that the industry, in the interests of economy, has developed modern processes of bread-making. These utilize the weak British flour but use certain additives to produce the everyday cut and wrapped standard white loaf, which, because of the additives, is a bread best avoided by the arthritic. If you are making wholemeal bread it does not matter so much whether the flour used is weak or strong, because when the bran is left in the flour the whole texture of the loaf is heavier and tighter anyway. There are several advantages in eating wholemeal bread. Not only do you get more fibre, which is an essential part of any diet, but the bread is much more satisfying and furthermore it is free from additives.

Rice

Fried rice is a good way of making a quick lunch or supper dish and, by knowing a little more about the different types of rice available, you can produce a variety of nutritious and tasty dishes.

Most people realize that there is a long-grained rice called 'Patna' which is used in savoury dishes, and a round-grained or 'Carolina' rice which is used to make puddings. The Patna rice comes to the table as separate fluffy grains, whereas the Carolina rice soaks up the liquid and produces a more sticky texture.

All rice starts off brown and the natural grain contains carbohydrate, protein and minerals and most of the vitamin B complex. When the rice is refined, the outer husk is stripped off and discarded and with this goes 80% of the vitamin B and a good proportion of the minerals; this is a waste of nutrient to say the least. With the husk removed, the grain is then rubbed and polished in leather-lined drums and sometimes talc and glucose are added to improve the whiteness and make the grain shiny. Sadly, nearly all the rice we buy today is the white polished variety.

When rice is only eaten occasionally this loss of nutrient is probably of no great significance, but with Dr Dong's diet it is likely that you will be serving rice much more often, so it does make sense to gain all the nutrient available by buying and cooking the unpolished brown rice.

Natural brown rice is obtainable from health food shops and supermarkets; it takes slightly longer to cook (about thirty-five minutes compared with twelve minutes or so for white rice), it has a much more interesting 'nutty' taste, and it blends well with vegetables and tinned fish.

Today many varieties of rice are available on the market and each has a characteristic flavour or quality. For special occasions it is worth paying a little more and trying Basmati or Pillao rice, or using Arborio rice for risottos. You can also use wild rice for a change or mix it with your usual variety (wild rice is actually a water grass, not a grain). All these varieties are available from specialist shops and supermarkets.

Soya bean products

Many soya bean products are now to be found on the market and they will help enormously in varying your diet. I have illustrated their use in the recipe section (Part II).

Soya beans

Dried soya beans can be bought in practically all health food shops and they contain the same amino-acids which make up the protein that is also found in meat. This makes them a true nutritional substitute for meat, eggs, milk, cheese, and they are also quite the cheapest food available.

Soya beans can form the basis for many tasty main-course dishes. Like most pulses, they benefit from overnight soaking and a long cooking time. A pressure cooker can be a great help in speeding up the whole operation. The cooked beans are then either mashed or blended in a food processor and when mixed with a variety of other vegetables, along with herbs or flavourings, it is possible to make rissoles, pâtés and burger-like dishes. Soya beans are now obtainable ready cooked and canned and are very suitable for use on this diet as they should not contain any additives – but do check the label.

Soya or soy sauce

Soy sauce was invented by the Japanese as a flavouring agent for their largely rice- and vegetable-based diet. It is made by fermenting the soya beans and the resulting black liquid is then filtered and bottled. There are various grades from thin dark brown to a thick black sauce, so it is worth experimenting to see which you prefer. However, do be wary and check the label carefully to see that it is in fact pure soy sauce with no additives.

Tofu

During the fermentation of soya beans a white, cheese-like curd is produced and this is now marketed as tofu. It is very bland and will absorb both sweet and savoury flavours. It makes an excellent base for pre-dinner dips to be served with crudités. A few years ago, when tofu was first imported into the United Kingdom, I was invited to a Japanese restaurant for its launch on to the British market. I sampled it in dozens of dishes – cold, hot, sweet, savoury – and I was amazed at its versatility. Try it, and if you find that you like it, then experiment. It is also available smoked, which gives it a bit more flavour. Just to get you going I have included a few tofu ideas in the recipe section, but there are cookery books which specialize in its use. A word of warning – when buying ready-made tofu dishes read the labels carefully to check for additives, etc.

Soya flour

Dried soya beans can be finely ground to produce soya flour. When the yellowish-looking flour is mixed in equal proportions with cooking oil it makes a very acceptable substitute for egg yolks and has many of the same properties in cooking. It can also be mixed with wheat flour in bread-making to produce a high protein bread. In addition it can be added to sauces and soups as a thickening agent.

Soya milk

Soya flour plus water produces soya milk. This can be used in place of cow's milk for all your needs. The taste is different but, as with everything, one can get used to it.

Allergies to cow's milk are very common, hence the increasing availability of soya milk in supermarkets as well as health food shops. Although it is best used in cooking, it can also be added to tea and coffee, although some coffees can make the milk curdle, which does not make the drink look very pleasant. However, with instant coffee there is one way round this problem: put the milk directly on to the coffee powder in the cup and then pour on the boiling water.

Soya cream

This is made by various manufacturers, some of whom use additives which are not acceptable to arthritics. However, have a look round, check the labels and see what is available.

Textured vegetable protein (TVP)

Apart from the flour and the milk, a textured vegetable protein is manufactured from soya beans. It can be flavoured and used as a substitute for meat and, as such, adds greater variety to this diet. These proteins are made commercially from soya flour, and look like dried foam. They are then textured to resemble mince or chunks of meat and are sold in health food stores. It is best to buy the unflavoured varieties as some of the flavoured ones contain monosodium glutamate and other artificial flavourings. Apart from the mince and chunks, 'spun' protein is also available. This is usually more expensive. It is made by treating soya with an alkali; then spinning it through small holes into an acid solution. The mixture is then shaped and moulded and made to look remarkably like steaks and pieces of chicken. These can be bought in various sizes and are really quite convincing. Obviously the taste is not exactly the same as meat, but it does make a welcome addition to this diet, especially when combined with vegetables and sauces in casseroles and stews.

All types of TVP need to be reconstituted before use; this makes it handle more like meat and allows it to be flavoured. Vegetable or chicken stock, or even a yeast extract, can be used as flavouring. The yeast extract makes the TVP 'meat' more 'beef'-like. Large pieces of TVP need to be soaked for two to three hours and the chunks for about half an hour to an hour, but the mince needs only a few moments.

It is recommended that TVP products should not be included in the diet at the very beginning, but should be gradually introduced when a marked improvement in your physical condition has been noticed. Soya products are increasingly being used by the food industry since they regard it as a valuable food source. Soya is likely to be developed further and used more and more in the future.

Quorn

In a diet where meat intake is limited alternative forms of protein are worth finding. Textured vegetable protein (TVP) has been on the market for some years and this does, to some extent, help fill the gap. But unfortunately this product does not appeal to everyone's taste. To put it politely – for some people it can create a certain amount of flatulence! Nevertheless, TVP is still worth trying because if it suits you, then you have gained an additional source of protein. On such a restrictive diet as this, every little plus is a step in the right direction.

However, in the past twenty-five years experiments have been made to find another suitable source of protein, and Quorn is the result. This product is now readily available in good supermarkets and health food shops. In appearance it actually looks like chunks of chicken. Although it is sold vacuum-packed and has a reasonable shelf life, it can also be frozen. It is a very good product to have at your disposal.

Quorn is totally vegetable in origin and its source is a tiny fungus, *Fusarium graminearum*, which grows naturally in soil. The commercial product is the result of a complex process which involves the addition of carbohydrate (in the form of glucose) plus oxygen, nitrogen and minerals. It is flavoured with natural vegetable extracts and egg white is added to form succulent little white-grained chunks.

Unfortunately Quorn is still relatively expensive but nevertheless well worth trying because of its versatility; it takes up whatever flavour you put with it and has the consistency of meat when chewed. Quorn is already cooked when you buy it so it can be added to dishes directly and just requires heating through. It is quite robust – if the recipe calls for a longer cooking time to allow the flavours of a sauce to develop, it can be cooked for 30–40 minutes without breaking up. As a consequence it can be used for casseroles and pies; it stir-fries well and can even be grilled. Try it. There are recipes in Part II to start you off and inspire you to experiment further.

Filo pastry

Filo pastry has been common in Greece for thousands of years. It is a simple type of pastry and it turns up in various forms in other cuisines around the world: for example, in Austrian apple strudel and Indian samosas. Basically it is very thin pastry made from flour, vegetable oil, a little salt and water and a lot of hard work to knead the dough to make the mixture so elastic that it can be stretched to an almost 'see-through' sheet.

Over the past few years filo pastry has become increasingly available in this country, initially through specialist shops and delicatessens, then health food shops, and now it is available deep-frozen in most supermarkets. The ingredients are fine for arthritics, and when brushed with vegetable oil or margarine instead of clarified butter this pastry proves a very versatile and useful addition to the diet. However, filo does vary from brand to brand – some are thinner than others; some come in large sheets and some in small – but more of a problem is that some brands now have preservatives added. So again – READ THE SMALL PRINT ON THE PACKET.

Because filo pastry is very thin it dries out quickly – especially in a hot kitchen – so only unwrap what you need just before use; keep the rest tightly wrapped and covered with a damp cloth.

You can brush the pastry with either oil or melted margarine and then bake in a moderate oven. It can also be used dry and then deep-fried. Either way it is an attractive and delicious alternative to heavier traditional pastries.

If you cannot find a pure filo without any additives in the way of preservatives (I have come across a brand imported from Australia with a 'Do not freeze' label on it and the preservatives it contained were horrendous!) then I suggest that you make your own (recipe no. 189). Don't worry if you can't get it wafer-thin – by using one layer only instead of several you can still make dishes such as samosas and spring rolls.

Nuts

Nuts are an excellent source of protein, fat, minerals and fibre. It is worth learning to use nuts in your savoury cooking as well as in sweet dishes.

Most nuts are acceptable and they can be used either whole or ground. The only exception to this is the use of 'processed' nuts, such as the roasted and salted varieties so beloved by nibblers. These nuts (usually peanuts) are acceptable within the diet until they are roasted and packed in little bags or tins, because during this processing flavour-enhancers like monosodium glutamate are added and they can cause pain to arthritis sufferers. However, it is possible to make your own salted nuts which are even more delicious than the processed varieties (recipes no. 180 and 181).

To get the best possible nutrition from the protein in nuts they should be eaten with a certain amount of carbohydrate, such as bread or potatoes; this is because the chemical interaction enables the body to assimilate the protein more easily.

Nuts have a reputation for being fattening and, admittedly, they do have a high fat content. Indeed the percentage of fat in nuts is higher than that in meat, but it is a vegetable fat and, in the main, it is a polyunsaturated fatty acid, which is better for you. However, cashew nuts have a large proportion of saturated fatty acids, more so than all other nuts, and therefore these should not be eaten too often.

Peanut butter is an excellent spread for bread, but do read the labels on the purchased variety to make sure they do not contain additives.

Pine kernels are becoming increasingly available not only in health food shops but also in supermarkets. They are rather expensive but they are delightful when added to pesto – a wonderful basil paste which hails from Italy and is fantastic with good-quality pasta. There is a recipe in Part II (recipe no. 173) for a version that can be used by arthritics. And toasted pine kernels are a delicious addition to salads.

Sunflower seeds

These seeds have a rather unusual flavour and hence are an acquired taste. However, like all nuts, they are nutritious.

Honey

There are many different varieties of honey, usually named after the plants from which the bees have gathered nectar. Honey is made up of fructose, glucose and sucrose with water; it also contains small amounts of dextrins, maltose, wax and protein. The comb honeys also contain the pollen. Honey is a useful addition to your larder as it can add variety to the sweet side of your diet which is limited due to the absence of fruit.

Honey is sweeter than cane sugar because it contains fructose which is one and a half times sweeter than the sucrose of cane sugar; it is also lower in calories gram for gram because of its water content. This is worth noting if you are overweight but have a sweet tooth.

It has been found that some honeys may aggravate your complaint;

if you do find that you have an adverse reaction after eating a particular honey, then do not eat it again.

Egg whites

The pure albumen in egg whites is a very simple protein and is perfectly acceptable within this diet. The egg yolk, on the other hand, is much more complicated and contains a fair amount of animal fat.

Most savoury and sweet dishes usually made with whole eggs can be made equally well without the egg yolk and, when the egg yolk is essential, such as in making mayonnaise, then a substitute can be made by mixing together soya flour and pure vegetable oil. This mixture has most of the properties of egg yolk and is a reasonable substitute for flavour.

Margarine, free from milk solids

Margarine is an emulsion of fat and water which is hydrogenated to make it hard, and then coloured and flavoured. To this mixture are added extra vitamins A and D to make it as nutritious as butter, and an antioxidant to prevent the fat from becoming rancid.

Supermarket chilling cabinets today bulge with different hard or soft margarines, low fat spreads and butter substitutes. Many are labelled 'high in polyunsaturates' or 'low in cholesterol'. Ignore the hype and read the labels carefully. Choose one that is made from 100% vegetable oil with natural flavour and colour and without any whey, which is the milk solid. Such margarines do exist, however hard they may be to find. Some arthritics seem to be able to tolerate small amounts of the more expensive luxury margarines and you may be one of the fortunate ones. If, however, you do not feel a lot better on the diet, then the margarine you are using could be the culprit.

A substitute for margarine which is worth trying if you cannot find one free from milk solids is a spread made from solid vegetable fat flavoured with a little rosemary. Melt some white solid vegetable fat and add to it a little corn oil and a few leaves of rosemary, allow this to go cold and use in place of margarine. A little salt can be added if you like.

At this point it is worth commenting on the label 'low in cholesterol' which can be frequently seen on margarines and spreads.

Basically, cholesterol is a part of the body structure and a normal constituent of the blood-stream. Your body lays down its own cholesterol from the foods you eat and for most people this amount is correct and poses no problem. But some people, by nature, lay down more cholesterol than is safe, and it is these people who run the risk of premature heart attacks if they do not watch their animal fat intake.

Cholesterol is only found in animal fat; it is not a natural constituent of plants and grains. In the recipes in Part II of this book animal fat is almost totally eliminated; the small amount of chicken you are permitted within the diet is very low in animal fat, and the fatty acids that are found in fish are largely unsaturated.

Unsaturated and particularly the polyunsaturated fatty acids that are found in plants and grains actually help in breaking down excess build-up of cholesterol. If someone in your family suffers from high cholesterol, then following the recipes in this book will be good for them as well.

In many ways the 'low in cholesterol' labels on margarines can be misleading. If a product is made from vegetable oil, it should not contain cholesterol anyway.

Seafood

Our islands are surrounded by water, yet the amount of fish eaten by the average person is only about 10% of the amount of meat consumed.

If you change to this diet, fish will appear much more regularly on your menu to provide you with your daily requirement of protein, therefore it is important to know a little more about this valuable food.

All fish are a good source of protein, minerals and the B complex vitamins. Also, fatty fish contain the fat soluble vitamins, A, D and E, and most fish are free from carbohydrate. Seafish are important because of the iodine they provide in the diet, and all fish contains phosphorus. When fish are eaten whole, as for example are sprats, the bones provide an excellent source of calcium.

All in all, a very valuable food, so why do we eat so little?

Fresh fish is expensive, but then so is meat. Really the main reason is availability. Unlike meat, fish must be eaten within one to two days of being caught, and the best fish is without doubt the freshest. Sadly, by the time the catch is offloaded from the boats, marketed and delivered to the inland fishmonger, it is nearly always a day or two old. This does not mean to say that this fish will do you any harm. It is far from being bad, but the fact remains that it is not quite as good as it was a few moments after it was caught. For those lucky people who live near the sea, there are delicious and numerous varieties of fish to choose from, but the rest of us can still enjoy the available fish by choosing and buying carefully.

If at all possible, get to know a fishmonger; he will be able to advise you on which variety to buy, when it is at its best. Some fish are very seasonal. These are listed in the seasonal cook's calendar in Part II of this book. These are not only at their best during their season, but they are also at their cheapest.

Choose your fish carefully. Firstly, look at the eyes; they should be bright, the gills should be red, and the scales still attached to a clearly marked body. The fish should have a fresh smell, rather like seaweed, and the flesh should look creamy white and moist. Having bought your fish, cook it as soon as possible after purchase because it does not store well.

Obviously the ideal is to buy fresh fish, but not everyone is fortunate enough to have a fishmonger near by, so the next best thing is preserved fish.

Fish can be tinned, frozen or smoked, and all these methods are acceptable, as long as certain points are noted.

When buying tinned fish, check the label to see that it is packed in pure vegetable oil; avoid all the varieties tinned in tomato or some other sauce. Many varieties of tinned fish are readily available and are useful to keep in a store cupboard.

Genuine smoked fish is fine, and this is where your fishmonger can guide you. So often today, dyes are used to produce the colouring in smoked fish, and these must be avoided. If the colour is running on a fishmonger's slab, then that is a sure sign that the fish is not correctly smoked, but dyed. True smoked fish does not stain the slab.

Finally, frozen fish. Freezing fish at sea is a superb way of getting really fresh fish to the consumer; the only nutrient you lose is a certain amount of vitamin B, which drips out when the fish is thawing. To minimize this, it is best to cook frozen fish straight from the frozen state. Of course, when we are talking of frozen fish, this does not include any of the frozen processed varieties. Fish fingers and fish coated in batter or breadcrumbs without doubt contain antioxidants and other additives which you must avoid.

Frozen fish has a freezer life of about two to three months. It doesn't go bad after this time, but it does lose much of its flavour.

Shellfish, including crustaceans like crabs and shrimps, and molluscs such as mussels and whelks, are also a good source of protein and add great interest to the diet. Unfortunately, the pickled varieties sold on the promenade at the seaside are not allowed. It is particularly important to buy shellfish really fresh and in season. Instances of food poisoning usually only arise when molluscs are gathered wild, particularly in the summer months; then there is a fear that they could be contaminated by sewage. But all kinds of shellfish purchased from a fishmonger are safe. In fact, food poisoning from fish is rare as fish generally become unpalatable when the conditions are right for the multiplication of food poisoning bacteria.

Fish contains no connective tissue, so it requires very little cooking, only sufficient heat is needed to coagulate the protein which turns the flesh white. When it is overcooked the flesh becomes dry, rubbery and unappetizing. Fish cooked in a liquid loses nearly half of its minerals, but all these can be recovered by using the poaching liquid as the basis for a sauce. Baking, frying and grilling cause little loss of nutrient except in the case of grilling very fatty fish, when the fat soluble vitamins A and D will be lost as the fat drips out of the fish.

Fish cooked in a microwave is particularly good. If it is frozen first defrost it and then place it in a suitable container. Arrange it so that the thickness is uniform throughout: that is to say tuck under the tail section so that it will not overcook. Season the dish as required (there is no reason why you should not experiment with different herbs such as fennel and basil) and then cover the dish with clingfilm. Remember to make a small slit in the film to let the steam slowly escape as it cooks. Microwave on full power allowing approximately 1 minute for every 100 g (4 oz) of fish. Always undercook slightly because the fish will go on cooking when you remove it from the oven. If the fish is very cold or very thick you may have to adjust the cooking time. Do bear in mind that timing is also dependent on the wattage size of your microwave – so you may have to check it by trial and error. The times I have suggested apply to a standard 600 watt oven.

Vegetable oils

A diet free from animal fat means that all the fat required for cooking and frying must be of vegetable origin. There are many different types of vegetable oil on the market and this causes confusion. Not only are there specific vegetable oils like safflower oil, sunflower seed oil, olive oil, etc., but there are also the non-specific ones like pure cooking oil or pure vegetable oil. The one thing to remember when buying oil for cooking is that you get what you pay for.

The specific oils are really the best buy. Safflower oil, sunflower seed oil, soya oil, corn oil, and groundnut oil all have a high percentage of polyunsaturated fatty acids and are known to lower the level of cholesterol in the blood. These oils are pure and each one has a distinctive taste. Safflower is best because it has the highest percentage of polyunsaturated fatty acids, and then you work down the list, but all these oils are ideal for cooking, frying and salad dressings.

Olive oil is also a pure oil, but it is very expensive and is best kept for use when its particular flavour is needed in a salad dressing, or for cooking a Mediterranean-type vegetable dish where the flavour of the oil enhances the overall taste.

Further down the scale come palm oil and coconut oil. Both of these are very high in saturated fatty acids and should be avoided in this diet.

Most supermarkets have their own blends of oil called pure vegetable oil, or cooking oil. These are usually cheaper and are a blend of a variety of oils, so they can be higher in saturated fatty acids than you want. They can also contain a proportion of rape seed oil, which has been known to cause heart damage to animals fed large amounts, so it is always best to avoid these oils and stick to the ones you can identify.

All oils are a rich source of vitamin E and they are also a good source of energy in the diet.

Solid vegetable fats can be used, but they are higher in saturated fatty acids, so their use should be restricted. Oil can be substituted in cake-making when normally a solid fat would be used.

Tea

There are many different teas on the market today, and it does seem a shame not to experiment more to find one that really suits your palate. Some towns have specialist tea and coffee shops where the teas are blended to suit the water in that particular area. These shops are well worth a visit, particularly if you decide to drink your tea without the addition of soya milk or sugar.

There are teas from Africa, as well as from India and Ceylon, and there are the large green-leaved teas from China. The China teas have a very delicate flavour and should never be drunk with added sugar or any kind of milk.

Tea is a very refreshing drink, and a good pick-me-up, it is best to have whatever kind of tea you drink rather weaker than usual, and to try it without sugar. The rule is to be able to see the bottom of the cup.

You will find that special teas are rather more expensive than the usual supermarket brands, but with a reduced milk and meat bill, you may be able to treat yourself to a very special tea.

Coffee

The effects of coffee, whether fresh, instant or decaffeinated, are very unpredictable for arthritics. Some people find that most types or brands cause a noticeable reaction, while others can drink virtually any variety without ill effect, so personal experimentation is necessary.

If you buy fresh ground coffee or beans, choose the darker kinds as they are less acidic, and should therefore be less detrimental to the drinker.

If you are unable to find any coffee that leaves you unafflicted, you may care to try dandelion coffee, which is made from the root of that weed; you can even make it yourself by roasting and grinding the roots. However, do not be put off if you don't enjoy the flavour of your first cupful.

Finally, beware of the side-effects of normal coffee; research has shown that it can cause depression and irritability, which may be fine for promoting after-dinner arguments, but does not help the arthritic.

Herbal infusions

These have gained in popularity now that research has indicated that too much caffeine – found in tea and coffee – can make one feel unwell, although naturally this does depend on the quantity and strength of the tea or coffee that is drunk.

I am a great believer in all things in moderation, unless there is a specific allergic reaction. Four to five cups of weak tea or coffee during the day should not be harmful.

However, if you are the sort of person who requires more hot drinks during the day, then shop around for a suitable infusion. You will need to avoid fruit, but camomile, mint, dandelion and many other varieties may be to your taste. There's also an added bonus in that many of these herbal drinks are beneficial to the body system and aid digestion, purify the blood, etc.

I have recently found that many health food shops sell individual '1-cup' packets, so you can experiment without ending up with 25–40 bags of a herbal infusion which you can't stand lying in your cupboard!

Soda water

The best way to obtain soda water is to make your own with a refillable syphon with gas bulbs. You can even omit the chemical tablet and produce plain sparkling water, which is a most refreshing drink, either by itself or with a little bourbon (rye whisky). You will find more ideas for using soda water in Part II.

Herbs

All types of herb are acceptable within this diet, and they can be used to enhance many dishes which would otherwise be rather plain. Some varieties can be grown from seed in your garden or allotment; they are usually hardy plants.

Two of my favourites are bay leaf (for soups and stews) and parsley (for general cooking and sandwiches). Parsley is particularly rich in calcium and vitamin C, especially in the stalk, which is often discarded.

Salt

Salt is a very important additive to our food. It enhances flavour and is also used as a preservative.

Table salt contains up to 2% of an anti-caking agent, which allows the salt to flow freely, and has no adverse effect in this diet. Most salt is iodized; this is an important factor because iodine, a trace mineral element which is essential for the correct functioning of many body processes, is not found in many foods. A deficiency of iodine results in a goitre.

Sea salt, which is natural salt, is fine if available, but this natural salt contains only a very small amount of iodine, and this is lost by storage. Some sea salts are iodized, in the same way as table salt, and this is the type which should be chosen.

Sugar

Sugar is acceptable within this diet. Your body can assimilate it and it should not give you pain. Having said that, you should also note that it will not do you any good either, and it is a food which can easily be excluded from a diet without any ill effects.

Sugar in various forms, such as glucose, fructose, maltose and lactose, as well as the pure sucrose of cane or beet sugar, is widely available in many foods, and leaving out the sucrose is not going to make the diet deficient in energy which is all sugar gives you anyway.

Commercially produced sugar is mainly made from beet or cane. The sucrose is broken down in digestion to fructose and glucose which the body absorbs into the blood-stream. Carbohydrate is its only nutrient and, when this is not all used up in energy, it is laid down in the body tissues as fat, which is not good for anyone.

Do not think that, by using brown sugar, as distinct from white sugar, you are getting anything better. You are not. Molasses, which remains when the sugar has been crystallized, does contain a trace amount of vitamin B and very small amounts of iron and calcium, but the minerals are derived from the machinery, and the lime used in manufacture, so they can hardly be accepted as a better food source.

If you have a sweet tooth, try to cultivate a liking for honey. Honey contains fructose, which is one-and-a-half times sweeter than the sucrose of beet sugar, so you will eat less and get the same degree of sweetness.

Sugar is used as a preservative and, of course, is used in cake and sweet-making, thus most people will use a certain amount regardless of its nutrient value. The brown sugars, particularly the raw cane sugar, have a most interesting flavour. If you do use sugar, experiment with the different types on the market. They may not do you any more good, but they can add more variety and interest to your cooking.

Chicken

The breast of chicken is very low in animal fat and is one of the simplest animal proteins. When you are beginning to feel the benefit from Dr Dong's diet, you can start to introduce chicken into your meals. It is best to start by adding chicken stock (recipe no. 1), and then go on to the actual chicken breast a little later.

Commercial chicken soups and stocks in powder or cube form must be avoided as all these preparations contain additives. It is not difficult to make your own stocks and soups and there are several recipes in Part II to show you how.

Wine in cooking

Wine is not used in everyday cooking all that often, but occasionally one likes to prepare a special meal, and then it is acceptable to add a little white wine to give an extra zing to a recipe. On special occasions a small glass of rye whisky is the drink which will give least problems, but do drink it with water or plain soda water; commercial ginger ale could cause considerable pain.

Crispbreads

These are very useful to have in the store cupboard, but when you buy them choose carefully. It is important to read the labels as some are made with milk derivatives and some have chemical additives. But there are suitable ones on the market. Again it's a case of reading the labels carefully when you are shopping.

How to Start the Diet

Having read all about the diet, the time has now come to get started. This will probably be a difficult step, but, with a bit of forethought, life can be made to seem as normal as possible.

It's a good idea to choose a date a week or so ahead, so that you will have time to choose your menus and get your shopping list all worked out beforehand. If at all possible, get the rest of the family interested in the idea because you will need their support and understanding for the whole project to get under way.

The first thing to do is to have a good look in your larder. Sort out all the foods not allowed on the diet and place them on one side. Put all the foods you can eat on a separate shelf, so that you can reach them easily, and they will not get muddled up with the forbidden things. To do this you will have to read all the labels on all the tins, jars and packets. You will be surprised at the number of chemicals you have on your larder shelves.

Having sorted out your larder, look through the list of foods you can eat, and make out your own list of the fish and vegetables you really like so that, during the first week of the diet, you can spoil yourself a little, then you will not notice the hardships so much. This may be an expensive way of going about it, and you will certainly not be able to continue spoiling yourself, but at least it will get the ball rolling.

The first week is probably the worst: after you begin to feel some relief, there will be no stopping you.

Below are a few ideas for the first week's menus; all the recipes and ideas are simple and they are all in the recipe section. As you progress on the diet you can branch out and try a few more complicated things and even adapt your own favourite recipes.

Good luck and bon appétit!

Suggested menus for the first week

Choose one breakfast, one light meal and one main meal. You must, of course, use margarine, soya milk instead of cow's milk, and buy or make your own bread free from additives.

Breakfasts

Wholemeal bread or white bread without additives. Toasted if you like, spread with a soft margarine.
Honey, marmite, or some other yeast extract can be used to spread on the bread; even golden syrup is all right as long as this does not become a daily occurrence. Peanut butter is another possibility.
Mushroom omelette
Cereals can be eaten, but check the packet first. Sweeten with honey or brown sugar and use soya milk or even water.
Muesli
Fluffy omelette
French toast
Porridge made with water and a pinch of salt. Serve with a knob of margarine (if liked) and brown sugar.

Light meals

Salmon sandwiches; try the salmon savouries as a hot version
Mushrooms on toast served with green salad
Fried rice with prawn crackers
Sardines on toast served with cucumber
Baked potatoes with egg white
Irish rarebit
One of the soups served with herb bread or croûtons
Corn fritters

Main meals

Baked fish with mushrooms, new potatoes, glazed carrots
Stuffed peppers with a green salad
Nut cutlets with onion sauce, potatoes and cabbage
Vegetable stir-fry
Fried fish and chips

Salmon or tuna fish salad
Macaroni surprise with salad or green vegetables

Puddings and sweets

Honey dreams
Alexandra biscuits
Carob custard
Drop scones with syrup
Meringues
Nutty biscuits

Part II

The Recipes

Introduction

It is very difficult to say exactly how many people each recipe will serve, because appetites do vary greatly. Also, it will sometimes depend on whether the chosen recipe is served as a main meal or as a light meal during the day. However, as a guide, the recipes will serve four average helpings unless otherwise stated.

Throughout the recipe section a number of cooking terms come up quite frequently and so, to avoid repetition, an explanation will be found below for those who are not familiar with the terminology.

Bain marie Basically this means a double boiler. The food being cooked is not in direct contact with the heat as it is surrounded by a jacket of water. A bain marie can be improvised by using a glass or heat-proof basin over a saucepan of boiling water. This is the best way of melting gelatine and it is also useful for keeping sauces hot.

To bind To mix together, so that all the ingredients will hold together in one mass. It is important not to get the mixture too wet, and egg whites or water can be used for this purpose.

To blanch To plunge vegetables into boiling water, either for a few moments to kill the enzymes which, if not destroyed, will in turn destroy the vitamin C content, or for longer periods to cook the vegetable through. Nuts, such as almonds, are blanched by pouring boiling water over the nuts and leaving them for 5–7 minutes. This will loosen the skin which can then be removed.

Browned breadcrumbs This is bread, white or brown, which has been allowed to dry in a cool oven until it is crisp and golden brown, and then ground. The grinding can be done in an electric blender, mincer, or by hand, by rolling the crisp bread between sheets of greaseproof paper. Fine breadcrumbs can be made by shaking the crumbs through a sieve. They will keep for several months in an airtight jar. The browned crumbs are used to coat foods which need to be fried. The coating of first egg white and then crumbs prevents the oil or fat impregnating the coated food.

To chop This literally means to cut into very small pieces. Parsley, for instance, is cut into very small pieces so that it can be sprinkled, but, in the case of vegetables, the size of the pieces can be reasonably large. To prevent the knife from being blunted, chopping should always be done on a special board.

To cream To beat together margarine and sugar until the mixture is very light and fluffy. This should always be done with a wooden spoon. This introduces air to the mixture and makes a lighter cake or biscuit.

To cut and fold A method of adding flour or egg whites to a mixture. A metal spoon should always be used, using the edge as a cutting blade. A cut is made down the centre of the mixture, and when the spoon reaches the bottom it is turned over slightly, so that the scoop side brings the mixture from the bottom up to the top. Adding flour or egg whites using this method prevents the air from being knocked out of the basic mixture. This is most important when sugar is added to a meringue mixture or flour to a sponge mixture.

Fresh breadcrumbs These are best made from day-old bread. The bread is crumbled, either in an electric blender, or grated on a hand grater. Unlike browned crumbs, these will not keep and need to be made freshly when needed. They are sometimes used to coat food for frying, but more often they are used as an ingredient for stuffings.

Marinade This is a seasoned liquid in which fish or vegetables are left to soak. The purpose of the marinade is to impregnate foods with the flavour of the ingredients used to make up the marinade. These ingredients can be wine or sometimes stock, flavoured with herbs or onions. The foods can be left in a marinade from 2–24 hours depending on the recipe.

To purée To make a smooth soup or sauce. The best purée is made by forcing the vegetables through a hair or metal sieve, but an electric blender will do the job much quicker, although the resulting purée may contain stringy pieces of vegetables which spoil the smoothness. A combination of both methods is a good idea.

To sauté To cook over a strong heat in fat or oil, shaking the pan frequently so that the food browns a little but does not stick to the pan.

To simmer A long slow moist method of cooking, usually for soups and stews. The pan should be placed on a high heat and brought to the boil, then the heat must be lowered so that the pan just bubbles very gently for the required length of cooking time.

To stir-fry   A method of cooking often applied to Chinese and Japanese dishes. All the ingredients need to be prepared beforehand by cutting into long thin pieces. A wok or frying pan is used in which a little oil is heated until very hot, so that when the vegetables and meat are added to the pan they immediately seal and make a sizzling sound. The whole pan is well shaken, or the ingredients stirred constantly during the short, vigorous cooking time so that the meat is only just cooked and the vegetables still crisp.

1
Soups and Starters

List of Recipes

1

Chicken stock

1 chicken joint or chicken
  carcass
1 onion, finely chopped
1 carrot, finely chopped
1 litre (2 pts) water
1 bouquet garni (see page 242)

This stock can be used as a basis for making most of the soups in this book, but it is also useful as a basis for other dishes and for flavouring TVP.

Place the chicken joint or carcass with the vegetables in a saucepan. Add the water and the bouquet garni and bring to the boil. Cover and allow the stock to simmer for 1½ hours.

Strain off the resulting stock and allow to cool.

This stock will keep in a refrigerator for up to 3 days, or it can be deep-frozen and used as required.

Note: Never add salt when making stock because, during the long cooking time, evaporation will take place and this can result in a concentration of salt. It is much better to add the correct amount of seasoning at the end of the cooking time.

2

Croûtons

2 slices white or wholemeal
  bread
a little corn oil

Cut the slices of bread into 6 mm (¼ in) cubes.

Heat the oil and fry the cubes of bread until brown and crisp. Drain on kitchen paper. The oil is at the correct heat (190°C) if the cubes of bread brown in 30 seconds.

These croûtons are good served with most soups.

3

Melba toast

Set the oven at 200°C, 400°F or Gas No. 6.

Cut wafer-thin slices of stale white or brown bread. Place the bread in the heated oven for 10 minutes until crisp, dry and curled.

Serve hot or cold with margarine.
Melba toast goes well with most soups.

4

Mushroom soup

25 g (1 oz) margarine
1 small onion, chopped
225 g (8 oz) mushrooms, sliced
25 g (1 oz) flour
250 ml (½ pt) chicken stock
(recipe no. 1)
375 ml (¾ pt) soya milk
salt

Melt the margarine in a saucepan and add the onion. Cook until soft but not brown.

Add the mushrooms and cook for a further 2 minutes.

Stir in the flour and cook for a further couple of minutes. Remove from the heat and gradually stir in the stock and the soya milk.

Return to the heat and bring to the boil; cover and simmer for 30 minutes.

Add a little salt, if necessary, and serve hot with melba toast (recipe no. 3).

5

Potato soup

450 g (1 lb) potatoes, sliced
2 medium onions, chopped
2 large carrots, grated
1.5 litres (3 pts) chicken stock
(recipe no. 1)
1 small teaspoon sugar
salt
a pinch of grated nutmeg

Place the vegetables in a large saucepan; cover with the stock and season with sugar, salt and nutmeg.

Bring to the boil and simmer for 1½ hours.

Serve with chunks of wholemeal bread.

Note: In spring and early summer, try adding about 6 finely chopped young nettle tops to the soup 10 minutes before it is ready. Nettles combine well with potato.

1 chicken joint (breast and
   wing)
scant 1 litre (2 pts) water
1 onion, finely chopped
a pinch of dried thyme
2 sprigs of parsley
1 bay leaf
salt
grated nutmeg
chopped parsley to garnish

Vegetables
2 carrots, sliced
2 sticks of celery, sliced
1 small potato, diced

6

Chicken and vegetable soup

Place the chicken joint in a saucepan; cover with the water and add the onion and the herbs. Cover and simmer for 1 hour. Add the vegetables to the pan and simmer for a further hour.

Remove the chicken joint from the stock, dice the flesh, and place in a clean saucepan.

Strain the stock over the diced chicken flesh.

Remove the bay leaf from the strained vegetables and either liquidize the vegetables or pass them through a sieve – or for a soup with more texture, mash the vegetables with a potato masher.

Add the resulting mixture to the stock and chicken in the saucepan.

Reheat the soup, season with salt and a little nutmeg, and sprinkle with chopped parsley.

Serve very hot with melba toast (recipe no. 3) or croûtons (recipe no. 2).

2 tablespoons oil from the tin of
   tuna fish
1 medium onion, chopped
50 g (2 oz) Patna rice
750 ml (1½ pts) vegetable or
   chicken stock (recipe no. 1)
50 g (2 oz) cooked sweet corn
75 g (3 oz) tin of tuna fish,
   flaked

7

Corn and tuna soup

Heat the oil in a saucepan and add the onion; fry until soft, then stir in the rice. Cook for 5 minutes, stirring occasionally. Stir in the stock, bring to the boil, cover and simmer for 25–30 minutes.

Place the contents of the saucepan in a liquidizer and liquidize until smooth, or force the contents through a sieve. Return this to the saucepan and add the sweet corn and the flaked tuna fish. Heat through, and simmer for 5 minutes. Serve very hot.

This makes a very good lunch, especially if it is served with croûtons (recipe no. 2).

8

Onion soup

225 g (8 oz) onions, thinly sliced
40 g (1½ oz) margarine
1 dessertspoon flour
750 ml (1½ pts) chicken stock (recipe no. 1)
2 bay leaves
salt

Fry the onions in the margarine until golden-brown and very soft. Do this slowly to get the maximum flavour from the onions.

Stir in the flour and cook for 5 minutes to brown the flour with the onions.

Remove from the heat and gradually add the stock. Bring to the boil and add the bay leaves, together with a little salt. Cover and simmer for 30 minutes.

Remove the bay leaves and serve the soup hot with crusty bread.

9

Asparagus soup

100–150 g (4–6 oz) fresh asparagus tips
15 g (½ oz) margarine
500 ml (1 pt) well-flavoured chicken stock (recipe no. 1)
1 dessertspoon cornflour
salt
soy sauce

Cut the asparagus into 6 mm (¼ in) pieces and fry these in the margarine.

Pour over the stock; bring to the boil and simmer for 30 minutes.

Pour the soup into a liquidizer and liquidize for 30 seconds. Strain through a sieve into a pan and reheat.

Blend the cornflour with a little cold water and add this to the soup, stirring all the time. Bring to the boil, add a little salt and a little soy sauce, if liked. Serve hot with croûtons (recipe no. 2).

Serves 2–3 people.

10

Celery soup

1 tablespoon oil
1 head of celery, scrubbed
1 onion, diced
2 potatoes, diced
scant 1 litre (2 pts) chicken
   stock (recipe no. 1) or water
1 bay leaf
½ teaspoon salt
chopped parsley to garnish

Heat the oil in a large saucepan and fry the vegetables for 2 minutes. Reduce the heat, cover the pan, and cook for 10 minutes to allow the flavours to mingle and until the vegetables are soft but not brown.

Add the stock, bay leaf and salt; cover and simmer for 1½ hours.

Strain off the soup, and either liquidize the vegetables or pass them through a sieve.

Return the vegetable purée to the soup, reheat and season if necessary.

Serve sprinkled with parsley, and croûtons (recipe no. 2).

11

Corn and lentil soup

1 medium onion, sliced
1 medium potato, sliced
100 g (4 oz) lentils
1 litre (2 pts) chicken stock
   (recipe no. 1)
200 g (7 oz) tin sweet corn
salt to taste
chopped parsley to garnish

Put the onion, potato and lentils into the stock in a saucepan. Bring to the boil and simmer for 30 minutes until the lentils are soft.

Strain off the stock into a clean pan, and place the lentils, potato and onion in a liquidizer. Add the contents of the tin of sweet corn and liquidize until smooth.

Return the mixture to the pan containing the stock and reheat. Season with a little salt to taste and serve the soup very hot, sprinkled with chopped parsley.

Croûtons (recipe no. 2) go very well with this soup to make it a substantial lunch dish.

---

4 leeks
25 g (1 oz) margarine
450 g (1 lb) potatoes, diced
25 g (1 oz) flour
1.5 litres (3 pts) chicken stock (recipe no. 1) or vegetable water
salt
1 blade of mace

12

Leek and potato soup

Trim the leeks, wash them well, and cut them into slices about 1 cm (½ in) thick.

Melt the margarine in a saucepan and fry the leeks until lightly coloured. Add the potatoes and cook for a further 5 minutes.

Stir in the flour and cook for 2 minutes without colouring the flour, and remove from the heat.

Gradually stir in the stock and return to the heat. Season with the salt and the mace, then cover and simmer for 1 hour.

Check the seasoning and remove the mace before serving.

You can make this soup into a purée (by using a liquidizer) but you may need a little extra stock to give it the consistency of a 'cream' soup.

13

Parsnip soup

25 g (1 oz) margarine
1 medium onion, roughly
    chopped
25 g (1 oz) flour
1 teaspoon mild curry powder
1 teaspoon ground cumin
750 ml (1½ pts) chicken stock
    (recipe no. 1)
100 g (4 oz) potato, roughly
    chopped
325 g (12 oz) parsnip, roughly
    chopped
1 teaspoon salt
chopped parsley to garnish

Melt the margarine in a large saucepan and add the onion. Cover and cook for 2 minutes.

Remove the lid, add the flour, curry powder and cumin and cook for 1 minute.

Remove the pan from the heat and gradually stir in the stock. Return to the heat and bring to the boil.

Add the potato and parsnip, season with salt and simmer the soup for about 30 minutes.

Liquidize the soup in a blender or pass it through a sieve.

Adjust the seasoning and serve sprinkled with parsley.

14

Corn on the cob

1 corn cob per person
salt
15 g (½ oz) margarine

Trim the cob of all its outer leaves and fibres and cook in salted boiling water for 15–20 minutes.

Brush with a knob of margarine and serve immediately.

15

Whitebait

225 g (8 oz) whitebait
25 g (1 oz) wholemeal flour
salt
oil for frying
parsley sprigs

Wash the whitebait in cold water and pat dry on kitchen paper.

Season the flour with a little salt. Dip the fish in the flour and then shake off any excess.

Heat some oil in a deep-fryer until very hot (190°C). Plunge in the fish, a handful at a time, and cook for 2–4 minutes until crisp and golden-brown.

Drain on kitchen paper and keep warm while the rest of the fish are being cooked.

Tie some fresh parsley into a bunch with a piece of cotton and, when the oil is hot, fry the parsley until crisp.

Drain and serve with the whitebait.

Serves 2–3.

16

Tuna and potato puffs

1 onion, finely chopped
325 g (12 oz) cooked mashed potato
25 g (1 oz) margarine
salt
grated nutmeg
200 g (7 oz) tin of tuna fish
2 egg whites

Set the oven at 180°C, 350°F or Gas No. 4.

Mix the onion with the mashed potato and the margarine; season well with salt and nutmeg.

Drain the fish from its oil, flake the flesh, and add this to the potato mixture.

Whisk the egg whites until stiff and fold them into the potato mixture.

Grease 4 ovenproof individual dishes, and pile in the mixture.

Bake in the heated oven for 30 minutes and serve with Melba toast (recipe no. 3).

17

Avocado and crab starter

2 avocado pears
105 g (4 oz) tin of crab meat
angostura bitters
salt
a shake of paprika
watercress to garnish

Cut the avocado pears in half lengthways, using a stainless steel knife so that the flesh will not be discoloured. Discard the stone in the middle and scoop out the flesh with a teaspoon. Do this as carefully as possible so that the skins are left in one piece. Neatly dice the flesh.

Drain the crab meat and mix with the diced avocado pears. Season very lightly with angostura bitters and a little salt.

Pile the mixture back into the avocado skins, sprinkle with a little paprika, and garnish with watercress. Serve with thin slices of brown bread and margarine.

Note: Avocado pears are ready to eat when the skin just gives a little under gentle pressure. If the pears are too hard, place them in a warm place and leave them to ripen for 2–3 days.

18

Artichokes with mushrooms

4 large globe artichokes
salt
4 tablespoons olive oil
2 cloves of garlic
100 g (4 oz) mushrooms, sliced
a pinch of dried thyme
1 lettuce

Trim off the stems from the artichokes, and wash the artichokes in plenty of water. Place them in a saucepan of boiling salted water. Cover and cook for 40–45 minutes, or until the leaves pull away easily. Drain the artichokes upside down and allow to go cold.

Heat 1 tablespoon of the olive oil in a small saucepan. Add the garlic and mushrooms. Cook for 5 minutes. Allow the mixture to go cold, then add the thyme, a little salt, and the rest of the olive oil.

Pull off and discard all the outer leaves of the artichokes until you come to the base which is surrounded by fine hairs. Remove the hairs and place the artichoke bottoms on a bed of lettuce. Pour over the mushroom and oil dressing and serve well chilled.

225 g (8 oz) button mushrooms
salt
1 clove of garlic
4 tablespoons dry white wine
2 tablespoons olive oil
a pinch of dried thyme or
    tarragon

19

2 sprigs of parsley
1 bay leaf

Marinated mushrooms

12 coriander seeds

Wash the mushrooms and place them in a saucepan. Cover with water and add a little salt. Bring to the boil, then simmer gently for 5 minutes. Drain the mushrooms and place them in a shallow dish.

Crush the garlic and place in an enamel saucepan. Add the rest of the ingredients. Bring to the boil and simmer for 10 minutes.

Strain this mixture over the mushrooms; cover the dish and leave to marinade for 24 hours.

When ready to serve, place the mushrooms in individual dishes and pour over a little of the strained marinade. Serve with crusty bread.

½ cucumber, peeled and diced
1 teaspoon salt
1 small onion, finely grated
1 dessertspoon chopped mint

20

2 tablespoons olive oil
a pinch of sugar

Cucumber and prawn starter

225 g (8 oz) peeled prawns
lettuce to serve

Sprinkle the cucumber with the salt and cover with a plate; leave on one side for 30 minutes.

Drain the liquid from the cucumber and add it, with the onion and the mint, to the olive oil. Add the sugar. Beat the mixture with a fork.

Mix together the prawns and the cucumber and place on a bed of lettuce on individual plates. Spoon over the dressing and serve well chilled with walnut bread (recipe no. 21).

4 slices day-old wholemeal
  bread
margarine
21
50 g (2 oz) walnuts, finely
  chopped
Walnut bread
salt

Spread the bread with margarine and remove the crusts.

Sprinkle the walnuts over the bread, and season very lightly with salt.

Place the slices on a damp sheet of greaseproof paper and carefully roll up the bread like a Swiss roll. Wrap the rolls in the damp paper for 20 minutes, so that they will not unroll when sliced.

Cut the rolls into 6 mm ($\frac{1}{4}$ in) slices and serve with the cucumber and prawn starter (recipe no. 20).

---

3 tablespoons oil
1 stick of celery, chopped
4 leeks, cut into 2.5 cm (1 in)
  pieces
375 ml ($\frac{3}{4}$ pt) chicken stock
22
  (recipe no. 1)
1 bouquet garni (see page 242)
Marinated leeks
10 coriander seeds

Heat the oil in a saucepan, add the celery and cook for 2–3 minutes; add the leeks and sauté for 2 minutes.

Add the stock, the bouquet garni and the coriander seeds, and simmer for about 15 minutes until the leeks are tender, but not broken.

Drain the leeks carefully and arrange them in a serving dish. Strain a little of the cooking liquid and pour this over the leeks.

Cover and chill well before serving.

Serve with crusty wholemeal bread for a starter, or lunch.

450 g (1 lb) monkfish
seasoned flour
250 ml ($\frac{1}{2}$ pt) batter (recipe no. 84)
oil for frying
garlic and ginger salad dressing (recipe no. 161) to serve

23

Mock scampi

Cut the monkfish into cubes and roll them in the seasoned flour.

Dip the monkfish cubes into the batter and ensure that they are completely coated.

Drop them into hot oil (190°C) and cook for 3–4 minutes until the batter is crisp and golden.

Place a small bowl of garlic and ginger salad dressing beside each table setting as an individual scampi dip.

675 g (1$\frac{1}{2}$ lb) potatoes, cut into 6 mm ($\frac{1}{4}$ in) cubes
100 g (4 oz) frozen peas, defrosted
2 tablespoons vegetable oil
1 medium onion, finely chopped
1 tablespoon grated fresh ginger root
1 teaspoon mild curry powder
1 teaspoon cumin seeds
1 teaspoon ground coriander
2 tablespoons crunchy peanut butter
salt
225 g (8 oz) filo pastry (recipe no. 189)
oil for frying

24

Vegetable samosas

Place the potatoes in cold water and bring to the boil. Boil for 5 minutes.

Add the peas and boil for a further 2 minutes. Drain and place on one side.

Heat the oil in a pan to 180°C. Add the onion and the ginger and fry for 2–3 minutes.

Add the spices and fry for 1 further minute.

Stir in the peanut butter and allow to melt and blend with the spices. Mix with the potatoes and peas. Season to taste with salt and leave the mixture to cool.

Unroll the filo pastry and cut it into 18 cm (7 in) circles. Fold each circle in half and dampen the straight edge on one side and bring sides together, forming a cone shape by sticking the two straight edges together.

Place a spoonful of the spicy mixture in the cone. Dampen the top rounded edge and seal down firmly. Make sure all loose edges are stuck down by brushing with water.

Deep-fry the prepared samosas in hot oil (190°C) and serve hot.

The samosas can be prepared in advance, deep-fried and allowed to go cold, then reheated for 15 minutes in a very hot oven.

Makes 24 samosas.

Note: If you make your own filo pastry (recipe no. 189), you will need 500 g (1 lb) flour for the amount of filling. There is no need to make the filo as thin as the commercial variety which means that you can use only one layer of pastry for each samosa.

---

1 dessertspoon oil
1 clove of garlic, crushed
1 teaspoon grated fresh ginger root
150 g (6 oz) mushrooms, chopped
100 g (4 oz) spring onions, chopped
100 g (4 oz) bean sprouts
100 g (4 oz) peeled prawns
15 g (½ oz) cornflour
1 tablespoon soy sauce
1 tablespoon water
150 g (6 oz) filo pastry (recipe no. 189)

25

Spring rolls

Heat the oil in a pan. Add the garlic and ginger and fry for about 30 seconds.

Add the mushrooms, spring onions, bean sprouts and prawns and stir-fry for about 2 minutes.

Blend the cornflour with the soy sauce and water. Add to the pan, stirring all the time. Cook until thickened.

Allow the mixture to cool.

Cut the filo pastry into broad strips, about 12 × 25 cm (5 × 10 in). Place a tablespoonful of the prawn and vegetable mixture on the end of a filo strip. Fold in 2.5 cm (1 in) on either side to enclose the mixture and then roll up like a Swiss roll. Dampen the top edge and seal the pastry firmly.

Deep-fry the spring rolls in hot oil (190°C) for 3–4 minutes until golden-brown.

Makes 8 rolls.

26

Prawn and mushroom purses

75 g (3 oz) margarine
100 g (4 oz) mushrooms, chopped
25 g (1 oz) flour
125 ml ($\frac{1}{4}$ pt) soya milk or fish stock
100 g (4 oz) peeled prawns
salt
$\frac{1}{2}$ teaspoon dried dill or 1 teaspoon chopped fennel leaves
225 g (8 oz) filo pastry (recipe no. 189)
50 g (2 oz) margarine, melted

Set the oven at 180°C, 350°F or Gas No. 5.

Melt 25 g (1 oz) of the margarine in a small pan. Add the mushrooms and sauté for 2 minutes.

Sprinkle on the flour and mix well. Remove from the heat and gradually pour in the soya milk or stock, stirring all the time.

Return to the heat and bring to the boil, to make a very thick sauce. Stir in the prawns. Season to taste with salt and add the dill or fennel leaves. Allow the mixture to cool.

Cut the sheets of filo pastry into sixteen 10 cm (4 in) squares.

Place one square on the work surface and brush with the remaining margarine, melted. Place another square of filo on top at an angle, to form a star shape.

Place a spoonful of the prawn mixture in the centre of the filo star and gently gather up the edges over the mixture to form a 'purse'. Press lightly into shape.

Repeat with the remaining filo squares.

Brush with melted margarine. Place on a greased baking sheet and bake in the heated oven for 15–20 minutes.

Makes 8 purses.

Note: If you decide to make your own filo pastry (recipe no. 189) for this recipe it is essential that you make it very thin.

27

Stuffed eggs

15 g (½ oz) margarine
100 g (4 oz) mushrooms, finely chopped
1 shallot, finely chopped
1 tablespoon chopped parsley
salt
4 hard-boiled eggs
salad leaves to garnish

Melt the margarine in a small frying pan.

Add the mushrooms and shallot and sauté until soft and dry. Stir in the parsley and season to taste with salt.

Cut the eggs in half lengthways. Scoop out the yolks and discard. Fill the cavities with the mushroom mixture.

Serve hot or cold with a salad garnish.

28

Vegetable cocktail

1 carrot, chopped
1 stick of celery, chopped
1 tablespoon chopped mint
¼ teaspoon dried oregano
a pinch of salt
1 teaspoon yeast extract
125 ml (¼ pt) water

Place the chopped vegetables in a blender.

Add the herbs, salt, and the yeast extract dissolved in the water.

Blend on a high speed for 30–40 seconds, then pour through a sieve to remove the stringy fibres from the celery.

Serve well chilled.

Serves 1.

Note: This cocktail is very rich in vitamins A and C.

100 g (4 oz) block of tofu
1 dessertspoon curry powder
1 dessertspoon peanut butter
a few drops of soy sauce

Crudités
A selection of the following:
cauliflower florets
cucumber wedges
carrot sticks
red, green or yellow pepper
    strips
mushroom slices
plain potato crisps

29

Crudités with tofu dip

Sieve the tofu or blend in a food processor until creamy in texture.

Beat in the curry powder and peanut butter and season to taste with soy sauce.

Place the dip in a small bowl and surround with a selection of the crudités.

2
Fish

List of Recipes

450 g (1 lb) white fish
salt
1 bouquet garni (see page 242)
2 tablespoons oil
1 clove of garlic, crushed
1 onion, thinly sliced
1 small green pepper, deseeded
   and thinly sliced into rings
1 tablespoon chopped parsley
150 g (6 oz) sweet corn (tinned
   or frozen)
250 g (9 oz) short crust pastry
   (recipe no. 186)

30

White fish and corn pie

Set the oven at 200°C, 400°F or Gas No. 6.

Wash the fish and place it in a saucepan. Just cover with water and season with a little salt and the bouquet garni. Cover, bring to the boil, and simmer very gently for 10 minutes or until the fish flakes easily. Remove the fish from the liquid, remove all skin and bones, and flake the fish.

Heat the oil in a frying pan, add the garlic, the onion and green pepper, and cook until soft. Add the parsley and season with a little salt.

Grease a 1 litre (2 pt) pie dish and place in it a layer of fish. Cover with a layer of vegetables and sweet corn and repeat the layers until all the ingredients are used.

Cover with short crust pastry and bake in the heated oven for 30–35 minutes until the pastry is golden-brown.

Note: Keep the liquid in which the fish has been cooked, as this can be used when a fish stock is needed.

31

Fish shells

325 g (12 oz) short crust pastry
  (recipe no. 186)
25 g (1 oz) margarine
25 g (1 oz) flour
250 ml ($\frac{1}{2}$ pt) soya milk or fish
  stock
225 g (8 oz) uncooked white
  fish, cut into small cubes
pinch of salt
pinch of powdered mace
1 dessertspoon chopped parsley

Set the oven at 200°C, 400°F or Gas No. 6.

Grease 6 scallop shells. Roll out half the pastry thinly and use to line the shells. Press in the pastry firmly so that the impression of the shells is made in the pastry.

Melt the margarine in a saucepan. Add the flour and cook for 2 minutes. Remove from the heat and gradually add the soya milk or fish stock, stirring all the time. Return to the heat, bring to the boil, and cook until thick.

Add the fish cubes to the sauce with the salt, mace and parsley. Allow the mixture to cool.

Divide the mixture between the 6 lined shells.

Roll out the other half of the pastry and cover the shells with pastry lids. Dampen the edges to make sure the lids stick firmly.

Bake in the heated oven for 15 minutes or until the pastry has set. Carefully unmould the pastry from the shells; turn upside down so that the shell markings are uppermost and return to the oven for a further 15 minutes until the pastry is golden-brown.

Serve hot or cold.

32

Tuna fish flan

Flan
50 g (2 oz) margarine
50 g (2 oz) vegetable shortening
150 g (6 oz) flour
2 tablespoons water

Set the oven at 190°C, 375°F or Gas No. 5.

Rub the margarine and shortening into the flour until the mixture resembles breadcrumbs. Add the water and mix to a dough.

Roll out the pastry and line a 20 cm (8 in) flan ring. Bake the pastry in the heated oven for 10 minutes (to prevent it from rising, prick the bottom, place a piece of greaseproof paper in the flan, and pour in a handful of dried peas or rice to weigh the paper down). Remove from the oven and make the filling.

Flan filling
25 g (1 oz) margarine
25 g (1 oz) flour
325 g (12 oz) tin of sweet corn
250 ml ($\frac{1}{2}$ pt) liquid from the tin of sweet corn
200 g (7 oz) tin of tuna fish
salt
2 egg whites
6 anchovy fillets

Melt the margarine in a pan; add the flour and cook until bubbling. Remove from the heat and gradually add the liquid from the tin of sweet corn. Return to the heat and cook until thick.

Add the tuna fish and sweet corn to the sauce and season with a little salt.

Whisk the egg whites until stiff and then carefully cut and fold them into the sauce, using a metal spoon.

Pile the mixture into the partly baked flan case and make a lattice of anchovy fillets on top.

Bake for a further 30 minutes until the mixture is risen and golden-brown.

Serve hot or cold with salads.

33
Bordered cod

450 g (1 lb) cooked cod
40 g (1$\frac{1}{2}$ oz) margarine
3 anchovy fillets
25 g (1 oz) flour
250 ml ($\frac{1}{2}$ pt) soya milk or fish stock
1 dessertspoon chopped parsley
100 g (4 oz) cooked shrimps or prawn pieces
450 g (1 lb) potatoes
1 tablespoon soya milk
salt

Remove the skin and bone from the cod and flake the flesh.

Melt 25 g (1 oz) of the margarine in a saucepan, add the anchovy fillets, and cook until the fillets are well broken up. Stir in the flour and cook for 2 minutes. Remove from the heat and gradually add the soya milk or fish stock, stirring all the time. Return to the heat and bring to the boil, cook until thick. Add the parsley, flaked fish and shrimps. Leave on one side.

Boil the potatoes in salted water until tender. Drain and mash. Beat in the rest of the margarine and 1 tablespoon soya milk to get a soft potato mixture. Season with salt. Pipe or pile a border of the potato around a shallow heated serving dish.

Reheat the fish mixture very carefully so that it does not break up, and pile into the centre of the serving dish.

Serve hot.

34

Tipsy cod

450 g (1 lb) fillet of cod
50 g (2 oz) mushrooms, sliced
40 g (1½ oz) margarine
125 ml (¼ pt) dry white wine
25 g (1 oz) flour
salt
450 g (1 lb) creamed potatoes
chopped parsley to garnish

Set the oven at 190°C, 375°F or Gas No. 5.

Cut the cod into 2.5 cm (1 in) cubes and place in a shallow ovenproof dish. Add the mushrooms, dot with about 15 g (½ oz) of the margarine, and pour over the wine. Cover the dish and bake in the heated oven for 25 minutes.

Melt the rest of the margarine in a saucepan; add the flour and cook for 2 minutes.

When the fish is cooked, strain off the liquid and add this to the flour and margarine mixture. Bring to the boil and cook until thick. Add a little water if the sauce is too thick (it should be of a coating consistency), season with a little salt and pour the sauce over the fish in the dish.

Cover with creamed potatoes and return to the oven to heat through and brown.

Garnish with parsley before serving.

35

Mary's fried rice

100 g (4 oz) brown rice
salt
75 g (3 oz) tin of tuna fish
2 tablespoons oil from the tin of
    tuna fish
1 onion, chopped
1 clove of garlic, crushed
100 g (4 oz) tinned sweet corn
1 teaspoon soy sauce

Cook the brown rice in salted water until just tender (recipe no. 36).

Place the oil from the tin of tuna fish in a large frying pan; add the onion and garlic and fry until soft but not brown.

Drain the rice and add this to the frying pan; stir the mixture so that the rice is well mixed with the oil and onion.

Add the tuna fish and sweet corn and heat thoroughly. Stir in the soy sauce, mix well, and serve hot.

Serves 2–3 people.

36

Brown rice

40 g (1½ oz) brown rice per
    person
salt
water
a little oil or margarine

Allow 450 ml (1 pt) water for every 50 g (2 oz) rice and add salt to taste. Bring to the boil in a saucepan.

When the water is boiling, add the rice and stir with a fork. Boil for 25 minutes until the grains are soft and tender.

Drain the rice and return it to the pan with a small amount of oil or margarine.

Shake the pan over a moderate heat to dry and glaze the rice.

37

Baked fish with mushrooms

50 g (2 oz) margarine
1 tablespoon chopped parsley
salt
450 g (1 lb) fillets of white fish
225 g (8 oz) mushrooms, sliced
2–3 tablespoons dry white wine

Set the oven at 180°C, 350°F or Gas No. 4.

Cream the margarine, mix in the parsley, and season with a little salt.

Place the fish fillets in a greased baking dish and cover with the mushrooms. Sprinkle over the wine and dot with the parsley butter.

Cover and bake in the heated oven for 20 minutes.

38

Trout amandine

4 trout (fresh or frozen)
1 tablespoon flour
salt
75 g (3 oz) margarine
1 dessertspoon oil
50 g (2 oz) flaked almonds
2 tablespoons chopped parsley

Dip the trout in the flour, which has been seasoned with salt. Brush off the excess.

Heat half the margarine and all the oil in a frying pan. When the mixture is hot, fry the trout until it is golden-brown on the outside and the flesh white. Do not overcook as this spoils the delicate flavour (about 4–6 minutes each side should suffice). Place the trout on a serving dish and keep warm.

Wipe out the frying pan with kitchen paper and place in the rest of the margarine. When the margarine is foaming, add the almonds and cook until golden-brown. Sprinkle in the parsley and cook for a further few seconds.

Pour the mixture over the trout and serve really hot.

39

Cod à la maître d'hôtel

450 g (1 lb) cod
salt
1 blade of mace or 1 bay leaf
50 g (2 oz) margarine
1 small onion, chopped
1 tablespoon chopped parsley

Place the cod in a saucepan, cover with cold water, and add a little salt together with the mace or bay leaf. Cover the pan and bring slowly to the boil, then simmer very gently for 10 minutes, or until the fish flakes easily.

Melt the margarine in a good-sized saucepan, add the onion and sauté for 3 minutes. Add the parsley.

Strain the fish and flake into large pieces, and add to the onion mixture. Very carefully toss the fish in the pan and reheat, taking care not to break it up too much.

Serve with mashed potatoes or rice.

Note: Reserve the fish stock and use when needed.

40

Herrings in oatmeal

4 small even-sized herrings
salt
100 g (4 oz) medium oatmeal
50 g (2 oz) margarine
1 tablespoon corn oil

Cut the heads from the herrings and split along the stomach. Clean the fish thoroughly if necessary. Open out the fish and place cut side down on a board and spread flat. Run your hand along the length of the fish, pressing firmly. Do this several times to press the bones away from the flesh. Turn the fish over and pull off the loosened backbone. Remove as many bones as possible, and trim off the fins.

Sprinkle the fish, inside and out, with salt and coat with the oatmeal.

Heat the margarine and oil in a frying pan and gently fry the fish for about 5 minutes on each side until cooked through and golden-brown.

Drain on kitchen paper and serve really hot.

Note: Mackerel can be cooked in the same way.

41

Curried prawn ring

2 tablespoons olive oil
1 onion, chopped
450 g (1 lb) long-grain rice
625 ml (1¼ pts) chicken stock (recipe no. 1)
25 g (1 oz) margarine
1 teaspoon curry powder
25 g (1 oz) flour
250 ml (½ pt) fish or chicken stock (recipe no. 1)
100 g (4 oz) frozen peas
100 g (4 oz) sweet corn
salt
225 g (8 oz) peeled prawns
chopped parsley to garnish

Heat the oil in a saucepan, add the onion, and cook for 2–3 minutes. Stir in the uncooked rice and fry for 5 minutes. Carefully pour in the 625 ml (1¼ pts) chicken stock, cover the pan, and simmer the rice for 20 minutes until all the liquid has been absorbed and the rice is soft.

Grease a plain ring mould and pack in the cooked rice firmly. Keep warm.

Melt the margarine in a small saucepan, add the curry powder, and cook for 1 minute; then add the flour and cook for 2 further minutes. Remove from the heat and gradually stir in the 250 ml (½ pt) fish or chicken stock. Return to the heat, bring to the boil, and cook until thick.

Cook the frozen peas and sweet corn in a little boiling salted water for 5 minutes. Drain and keep on one side.

Add to the sauce the prawns, peas and sweet corn. Simmer for 5 minutes and season with a little salt.

Carefully unmould the rice on to a serving dish, and spoon the prawn mixture into the centre of the ring. Sprinkle the top with a little parsley before serving.

Serve with a mixed or green salad (recipe no. 149).

42

Paella

about 450 ml (15 fl oz) chicken stock (recipe no. 1)
a few strands of saffron or a pinch of turmeric
450 g (1 lb) mussels, well-scrubbed and beards removed
2 tablespoons olive oil
1 large onion, chopped
1 clove of garlic, crushed
2 chicken breasts, cut into strips
225 g (8 oz) monkfish, cut into cubes
1 small green pepper, deseeded and sliced
1 small red pepper, deseeded and sliced
225 g (8 oz) Patna rice (or any long-grain rice)
8 whole prawns in shell
100 g (4 oz) peeled prawns
100 g (4 oz) frozen peas

Heat the chicken stock and pour it over the saffron or turmeric. Allow to stand for a few minutes. This will flavour the stock and turn it a bright yellow.

Check the mussels and discard those that do not close when tapped. (For more information about mussels see recipe no. 43.)

Heat the oil in a lidded pan large enough to hold all the ingredients, and fry the onion and garlic for 2 minutes.

Stir in the chicken strips and sauté them until they turn white. Add the monkfish, peppers and rice. Stir until all is well mixed and coated in oil.

Pour over enough stock just to cover the rice, saving a little for later. Bring to the boil, cover the pan tightly and allow to simmer very gently for 10 minutes, by which time the rice should be nearly cooked and the stock absorbed.

Add the rest of the stock to moisten the mixture and stir in the mussels. Cover again and cook over a high heat, shaking the pan gently for a further 3–4 minutes until the mussels are open. Discard any mussels that have not opened.

Finally, add the whole and peeled prawns and the frozen peas. Cover and cook gently until all the liquid has been absorbed and the peas are cooked and the prawns heated through – about 3–4 minutes.

Serve immediately with crusty bread and a green salad (recipe no. 149).

43

Mussels

2 kg (4 lb) fresh mussels
salt
375 ml ($\frac{3}{4}$ pt) water or 250 ml
  ($\frac{1}{2}$ pt) water and 125 ml ($\frac{1}{4}$ pt)
  dry white wine
1 onion, diced
1 small carrot, diced
2 sprigs of parsley
1 dessertspoon cornflour
chopped parsley to garnish

Place the mussels in a large bowl and cover with cold water, add a little salt, and leave until ready to cook. Carefully examine the mussels and throw away any with cracked or broken shells, or any which are open and do not shut immediately when tapped. Scrub the mussels with a stiff brush and remove the black breathing apparatus which is fixed to the side of the shell. This is usually called the 'beard'.

In a large saucepan place the water or water and wine, if used, and add the vegetables and the parsley. Bring this mixture to the boil and simmer for 10 minutes.

Place half the mussels in the pan, cover tightly, and allow to cook for 3–5 minutes, shaking the pan from time to time. At the end of this time remove them and cook the rest of the mussels. At the end of 3–5 minutes' cooking they will have opened; any that have not opened must be discarded.

Remove the mussels from their shells and place in a soup tureen. Cover with a cloth to prevent them drying out, and also to keep them warm.

Strain the cooking water through a muslin cloth into a clean saucepan. Mix the cornflour to a thin cream with a little water and add this to the saucepan. Bring to the boil, stirring all the time. Pour this over the mussels and sprinkle with parsley.

Serve with crusty bread.

Note: Mussels must be bought fresh and cooked on the same day.

44

Herby haddock

4 large fillets of haddock
3 tablespoons oil
1 tablespoon dry white wine
½ teaspoon salt
1 tablespoon chopped parsley
¼ teaspoon dried thyme or a few sprigs of fresh thyme
1 bay leaf
1 small onion, sliced

Place the haddock fillets in a shallow dish. Combine the oil and wine and add the salt and herbs to make a marinade.

Sprinkle the onion over the fish and pour over the marinade. Cover and leave in the refrigerator for at least 4 hours.

When ready to cook, drain the fillets from the marinade and place them under a preheated medium grill until the fish flakes easily. During cooking brush the fillets several times with the marinade.

4 thick slices of hake
2 onions, sliced
salt
50 g (2 oz) fine oatmeal
25 g (1 oz) margarine
1 tablespoon oil
1 large parsnip, diced

For the fish stock
1 carrot, chopped
1 onion, chopped
the trimmings from the fish;
   skin, bone, etc.
500 ml (1 pt) water
1 bay leaf
1 sprig of parsley
1 sprig of thyme

45

Baked hake

Set the oven at 180°C, 350°F or Gas No. 4.

First make the fish stock, unless you have some available from a previous recipe.

Add the carrot and onion, with the fish trimmings, to the water. Add the herbs and bring slowly to the boil. Cover and simmer for 30 minutes.

Rub the slices of fish with a cut piece of onion and sprinkle them with salt. Dip the fish into the fine oatmeal so that it is well coated.

Heat the margarine and oil in a frying pan and fry the fish until golden-brown, but not cooked through. Remove the fish from the pan and place in a casserole.

Fry the onion and parsnip in the rest of the fat until golden-brown.

Add the vegetables to the fish in the casserole and pour over the strained court-bouillon.

Cover and bake in the heated oven for 40 minutes.

46

Mackerel with cucumber

4 mackerel
75 g (3 oz) margarine
1 small cucumber, sliced
salt
2 tablespoons dry white wine
chopped fennel leaves to
  garnish

Set the oven at 200°C, 400°F or Gas No. 6.

Remove the heads from the cleaned fish.

Grease a large shallow ovenproof dish with 25 g (1 oz) of the margarine.

Use half the cucumber slices to cover the base of the dish. Place the mackerel on top of the cucumber and cover with the rest of the slices. Season with a little salt, and dot with another 25 g (1 oz) of the margarine and pour the wine over it.

Cover the dish with foil or a lid, and bake for 30 minutes.

When cooked, arrange the fish and the cucumber on a serving dish and keep warm.

Strain the juices from the fish into a small saucepan, bring to the boil, and boil rapidly, adding the remaining 25 g (1 oz) margarine, a little at a time. When the liquid has reduced by half, pour over the mackerel.

Garnish with fennel leaves and serve hot.

47

Foiled fish

2 dessertspoons oil
450 g (1 lb) white fish fillets
salt
100 g (4 oz) mushrooms, sliced
2 teaspoons chopped lemon
  balm or parsley

Set the oven at 190°C, 375°F or Gas No. 5.

Cut pieces of kitchen foil, each one twice the size of each fillet, and brush with a little of the oil.

Lay a fillet of fish on each piece of foil, sprinkle with a little salt, and cover with the mushrooms. Sprinkle over the herbs and pour on just a little oil. Parcel up the foil to make neat packages, and seal the edges firmly, so that none of the natural juices are lost.

Bake in the heated oven for 20 minutes (30 minutes for thick fillets of fish).

It is nice to serve the parcels unopened, so that they get to the table really hot with all their juices still in the package.

4 trout
a little flour seasoned with salt
50 g (2 oz) margarine
1 tablespoon oil
parsley sprigs to garnish

For the stuffing
1 onion, finely chopped
50 g (2 oz) mushrooms, chopped
25 g (1 oz) margarine
3 tablespoons fresh
    breadcrumbs
1 teaspoon dried mixed herbs
salt

48

Stuffed trout

Remove the bones from the trout or ask your fishmonger to do this for you.

Prepare the stuffing by frying the onion and mushrooms in the margarine. When really soft, stir in the breadcrumbs and mixed herbs and season with salt. Leave on one side to cool.

Fill the inside of the trout with the stuffing and then re-shape the fish. Roll the trout in the seasoned flour and brush off any excess.

Heat the margarine and oil in a frying pan and, when foaming, fry the trout until golden-brown on each side.

Drain on kitchen paper and serve hot, garnished with parsley.

1 tablespoon olive oil
1 kg (2 lb) middle-cut fresh
   salmon

For the court-bouillon
trimmings from the salmon
1 sprig of parsley
1 sprig of thyme
1 small onion, chopped
1 carrot, chopped
1 bay leaf
salt
1 litre (2 pts) water

49

Poached salmon

Place all the ingredients for the court-bouillon in a large saucepan. Bring to the boil, cover and simmer for 30 minutes.

Add the oil to the court-bouillon and gently lower in the salmon in one piece. Cover the pan and poach carefully for 35 minutes. Do not let the fish boil rapidly as this will break the flesh. When the fish is cooked it will be bright pink and will flake easily.

Serves 6 people.

Note: Fresh English salmon is best for this dish.

To serve hot
Drain the fish from the court-bouillon. Remove the skin and place the fish on a heated serving dish. Use the court-bouillon to make a parsley sauce (recipe no. 50) and serve with new potatoes and fresh peas.

To serve cold
Allow the fish to cool to blood heat in the court-bouillon, then carefully remove and drain. Take off the skin and garnish the fish with cucumber slices. Chill in the refrigerator until needed. Serve with a green salad (recipe no. 149).

25 g (1 oz) margarine
25 g (1 oz) flour
250 ml (½ pt) court-bouillon
2 tablespoons chopped parsley
salt
grated nutmeg

50

Parsley sauce

Melt the margarine in a small saucepan and add the flour. Cook for
2 minutes without colouring the flour and remove from the heat.
Gradually stir in the strained court-bouillon; return to the heat, and
cook until the sauce has thickened, stirring all the time.

Add the parsley and season with a little salt and nutmeg.

Serve with hot salmon or other fish.

40 g (1½ oz) margarine
2 tablespoons fresh
    breadcrumbs
1 dessertspoon chopped parsley
¼ teaspoon dried mixed herbs
salt
grated nutmeg
4 large fillets of sole
2 tablespoons browned
    breadcrumbs

51

Baked fillets of sole

Set the oven at 190°C, 375°F or Gas No. 5.

Melt 25 g (1 oz) of the margarine in a saucepan. Remove from the
heat and add the fresh breadcrumbs and the herbs. Season with salt
and a little nutmeg and mix well.

Skin the fillets of sole and spread the skinned side with the
breadcrumb and herb mixture. Fold the fillets in half, enclosing the
stuffing.

Grease a baking dish and put in the folded fillets. Sprinkle the fish
with browned breadcrumbs and dot with the rest of the margarine.
Bake in the heated oven for 30 minutes until the breadcrumbs are
crunchy and the fish cooked so that it flakes easily.

4 red or grey mullet, about
   150 g (6 oz) per person
4 small sprigs of rosemary
4 bay leaves
4 sage leaves
50 g (2 oz) margarine
100 g (4 oz) mushrooms, sliced
salt
4 dessertspoons dry white wine
   (optional)

52

Parcelled mullet

Ask the fishmonger to clean and scale the mullet.

Set the oven at 190°C, 375°F or Gas No. 5.

Stuff each fish with the whole herbs and a piece of margarine and grease a piece of kitchen foil for each fish.

Place the fish on the greased foil and cover with mushrooms. Sprinkle with a little salt and pour over the wine, if used. Parcel up the fish and seal well so that none of the juices escape.

Bake in the heated oven for 25 minutes.

---

4 large fillets of haddock
1 dessertspoon oil
salt
2 tablespoons chopped parsley
½ teaspoon dried basil
flour for coating
25 g (1 oz) margarine
1 tablespoon oil
100 g (4 oz) mushrooms, sliced

53

Basil's fillets

Place the haddock fillets on a flat plate and brush them on both sides with the dessertspoon of oil. Sprinkle with a little salt and 1½ tablespoons of the chopped parsley. Lastly, sprinkle with the basil. Cover and leave in a cool place for at least 30 minutes, longer if possible, for the fillets to absorb the flavour of the herbs.

When ready to cook, dip the fillets into flour until evenly coated, with the herbs still sticking to the fish.

Heat the margarine and 1 tablespoon oil in a frying pan and fry the fillets until golden-brown on both sides. Do not overcook. Keep warm.

If necessary, add a little more margarine to the pan, and slide in the mushrooms. Sprinkle over the remaining parsley, stir, then cover the pan and allow the mushrooms to cook in their own juice for 5 minutes.

Place a spoonful of the mushroom mixture on each fillet and serve with potatoes and a green vegetable.

54

Baked sea bream

1 large bream, 1 kg (2 lb)
4 tablespoons oil
1 onion, chopped
100 g (4 oz) fresh breadcrumbs
1 tablespoon chopped parsley
1 teaspoon chopped thyme
salt

Ask the fishmonger to clean and scale the bream. One whole bream weighing 1 kg (2 lb) will serve 4–6 people.

Set the oven at 190°C, 375°F or Gas No. 5.

Heat 1 tablespoon of the oil in a small saucepan and fry the onion until soft and transparent, but not brown.

Stir in the breadcrumbs and the chopped herbs and season lightly with salt.

Fill the cavity of the bream with the stuffing mixture.

Grease a large baking dish and place in the whole fish. Sprinkle with salt and pour the rest of the oil over.

Bake in the heated oven for 45 minutes, basting frequently, until the fish is cooked and will flake easily, and the skin is crisp and golden-brown.

Note: Whole bass and brill may be cooked in the same way.

25 g (1 oz) margarine
1 clove of garlic, crushed
1 tablespoon chopped chives
1 tablespoon chopped parsley
50 g (2 oz) mushrooms, sliced
2 tablespoons flour
125 ml ($\frac{1}{4}$ pt) dry white wine
3 tablespoons fish stock or
  water
salt
4 fillets of cod
oil for frying

55

Cod italien

Melt the margarine in a saucepan and add the garlic, chives, parsley, and mushrooms. Cook for 3 minutes. Add half the flour and cook for 2 further minutes.

Mix together the wine and stock or water and gradually add this to the vegetable and herb mixture, stirring all the time. Season with salt and bring to the boil, then simmer for 10 minutes.

Dip the cod fillets in the rest of the flour to which has been added a little salt. Heat some oil in a frying pan and fry the cod fillets until golden-brown.

Drain the fish on kitchen paper and place on a heated serving dish. Pour over the sauce and serve immediately.

450 g (1 lb) cod
salt
1 tablespoon flour
50 g (2 oz) margarine
1 onion, sliced
1 clove of garlic, crushed
1 dessertspoon curry powder
500 ml (1 pt) fish (recipe no. 45)
  or chicken stock (recipe
  no. 1)

56

Curried cod

Set the oven at 180°C, 350°F or Gas No. 4.

Cut the cod into 4 cm (1$\frac{1}{2}$ in) squares. Mix the salt with the flour and dip the cod pieces in this mixture.

Melt half the margarine in a frying pan and quickly fry the pieces of fish until golden-brown, but not cooked through. Place the fish in a casserole.

Put the rest of the margarine in the pan, add the onion and garlic and cook until golden-brown. Sprinkle in the curry powder and any flour left over from coating the fish and cook for 2 minutes.

Remove from the heat and stir in the stock, a little at a time. Return to the heat and bring to the boil.

Pour this sauce over the fish and place in the heated oven for 20 minutes to cook the fish through and to develop the curry flavour.

Serve with plain boiled rice (recipe no. 57).

57

Patna or long-grain white rice

40 g (1½ oz) Patna or other long-grain white rice per person
water
a pinch of salt

Place the rice in a saucepan with a tight-fitting lid and rinse with several changes of cold water to remove excess starch. Drain well.

Level the rice in the bottom of the saucepan, and measure how far it comes up the pan. (This can be easily done by poking your index finger into the rice and seeing how far the rice comes up your finger.) Add water to double the depth of the rice.

Add the salt, cover the pan tightly, place on a high heat and bring to the boil. As soon as the steam begins to escape, turn down the heat to very low and move the pan to one side of the hob. Time cooking for exactly 12 minutes. Do not remove the lid during this time as this releases the steam in which the rice is cooking.

At the end of 12 minutes, remove the lid and fork up the rice to separate the grains, which will be just soft and fluffy, but not sticky.

Note: The smaller the pan you use for small quantities of rice, the better the result will be. Also, measuring the water correctly is most important, as too much means there will be water still left in the pan at the end of the cooking time, and too little will not cook the rice.

For parties, or when large amounts of rice are needed, cook the rice in 325 g (12 oz) batches and allow each batch to go cold. Pile on to serving dishes, dot with margarine or sprinkle with a little oil, and cover with foil. When needed, reheat in the oven set at 190°C, 375°F or Gas No. 5 for 20 minutes until heated through. Fluff up with a fork and serve.

58

Grilled mackerel fillets

1 medium mackerel per person,
   about 325 g (12 oz)
15 g (½ oz) margarine, melted, or
   a little oil
sprigs of parsley to garnish

Ask your fishmonger to fillet the mackerel.

Brush both sides of the mackerel fillets with the melted margarine or oil.

Heat the grill and line the grill pan with kitchen foil, to prevent the smell of the mackerel getting on to the grill rack.

Grill the fillets, flesh side up, for 5 minutes. Turn the fish over and grill the skin side for a further 5 minutes. Finally turn the fish over again and grill the flesh side for a further 3–5 minutes until golden-brown.

Place the fish on a heated serving plate and pour over the fish juices from the foil. Garnish with parsley and serve hot.

Any grilled mackerel not eaten hot can be piled on to toast and served as a delicious snack.

59

Baked hake steaks

4 hake steaks, about 150 g
   (6 oz) each
flour
salt
1 small onion, finely chopped
1 teaspoon chopped parsley
1 tablespoon oil

Set the oven at 180°C, 350°F or Gas No. 4.

Place the hake steaks in a greased baking dish. Dredge with flour, season with salt and sprinkle over the onion and parsley. Sprinkle over the oil and cover the dish with a lid or foil.

Bake in the heated oven for 20 minutes. Remove the foil and increase the heat to 200°C, 400°F or Gas No. 6. Cook for a further 10 minutes to brown the steaks.

Place the hake on a heated serving dish and strain over the liquid from the cooking dish.

4 herrings
1 tablespoon fresh breadcrumbs
a little water
50 g (2 oz) shrimps, chopped
1 anchovy fillet, mashed
salt
1 egg white, beaten
browned breadcrumbs for
   coating
25 g (1 oz) margarine

60

Stuffed herrings

Set the oven at 190°C, 375°F or Gas No. 5.

Remove the heads and fins from the cleaned herrings. Flatten out the fish cut-side down, on a board. Using firm pressure, rub the flat of your hand up and down the backbone to press it away from the flesh. Turn the fish over and pull off the backbone and as many other bones as possible.

Soak the fresh breadcrumbs in a little water until soft. Add the shrimps to the fresh breadcrumbs, then mix in the anchovy fillet. Season with a little salt if necessary.

Spread a layer of the stuffing over the inside of the herrings and, starting at the head end, roll up the fish and secure with a skewer.

Dip the rolled fish in the egg white and roll them in the browned breadcrumbs.

Place the fish in a greased baking dish, dot with the margarine, and bake in the heated oven for 30–35 minutes until golden-brown.

salt
flour
4 large fillets of sole
50 g (2 oz) margarine
1 dessertspoon oil
1 dessertspoon finely chopped
   dill leaves or $\frac{1}{2}$ teaspoon dried
   dill

61

Fried fillets of sole

Add a little salt to the flour and dredge the sole fillets until evenly but lightly covered.

Heat half the margarine and the oil in a frying pan and gently fry the fillets until golden-brown on each side. Drain on kitchen paper and keep warm.

Wipe out the pan with kitchen paper and melt the rest of the margarine. When foaming, add the dill. Cook for no more than 30 seconds, then pour the flavoured margarine over the fish. Serve immediately.

15 g (½ oz) margarine
4 anchovy fillets
450 g (1 lb) cod fillets

For the egg sauce
50 g (2 oz) margarine
25 g (1 oz) flour
125 ml (¼ pt) dry white wine
  plus 125 ml (¼ pt) water
or 250 ml (½ pt) soya milk
2 hard-boiled egg whites, sliced

For the potato topping
675 g (1½ lb) potatoes
salt
25 g (1 oz) margarine
grated nutmeg

62

Prince's fish pie

Set the oven at 180°C, 350°F or Gas No. 4.

Melt 15 g (½ oz) margarine in a small pan, put in the anchovies and cook until the margarine and the anchovies are well blended. Set on one side.

Make the egg sauce. In another pan melt 25 g (1 oz) margarine and stir in the flour. Cook until the mixture bubbles. Remove from the heat and gradually add in the wine and the water or soya milk. Return to the heat and cook until thick.

Beat in the remaining 25 g (1 oz) margarine. Add the egg whites to the mixture and mix well.

Cook the potatoes in boiling salted water, drain and mash them with the margarine, and season with a little nutmeg.

Grease a pie dish with margarine or oil and place half the egg sauce mixture on the bottom. On top of this place the cod fillets and on top of the cod spread the anchovy mixture. Cover with the remaining egg sauce.

Pipe or pile the potato on top of the fish and bake in the heated oven for 45–50 minutes until the top is crisp and brown.

225 g (8 oz) cooked white fish
225 g (8 oz) cooked potatoes,
  mashed
1 tablespoon chopped parsley
salt
grated nutmeg
flour
1 egg white
browned breadcrumbs
oil for frying

63

Fish croquettes

Flake the fish and mix with the potato. Add the parsley and season
well with salt and nutmeg. Mix well and allow the mixture to get cold.

Divide the mixture into 8 and shape each piece into a cork-shaped
croquette or a round flat cake and coat in flour.

Dip the croquettes in the egg white and then in the browned
breadcrumbs. Press the coating on well.

Fry the croquettes in hot oil until golden-brown. Drain on kitchen
paper and serve really hot.

4 trout
1 onion, sliced
100 g (4 oz) mushrooms, sliced
125 ml ($\frac{1}{4}$ pt) dry white wine
1 sprig of parsley
2 bay leaves
1 sprig of thyme
1 clove
1 blade of mace
25 g (1 oz) margarine
25 g (1 oz) flour
salt

64

Trout in wine

Set the oven at 180°C, 350°F or Gas No. 4.

Remove the heads from the cleaned trout. Place the fish in a
shallow ovenproof dish and add the onion and mushrooms. Pour over
the wine and add the herbs and spices. Cover the dish and bake in the
heated oven for 20 minutes.

Melt the margarine in a small pan and add the flour. Cook for
2 minutes.

Drain the fish from the liquid and place on a heated serving dish.

Strain the liquid and stir this into the margarine and flour mixture, a little at a time. Bring to the boil and add a little more water if necessary to make the sauce of a pouring consistency.

Check the seasoning, and add a little salt if necessary. Pour over the trout and serve hot.

---

25 g (1 oz) margarine
1 large onion, finely chopped
100 g (4 oz) mushrooms, finely chopped
2 tablespoons fresh breadcrumbs
$\frac{1}{2}$ teaspoon dried mixed herbs
salt
4 middle-cut cod steaks on the bone
2 tablespoons dry white wine or water

65

Stuffed cod steaks

Set the oven at 180°C, 350°F or Gas No. 4.

Melt the margarine in a saucepan, add the onion and sauté for 3 minutes until soft. Add the mushrooms and cook for a further 5 minutes.

Remove from the heat and add the breadcrumbs and herbs. Mix well and season with a little salt.

Remove the bones from the centre of the cod steaks and fill the cavities with the stuffing. Re-form the steaks and fasten with cocktail sticks.

Place the steaks in a greased baking dish, and pour round a little wine or water. Cover with foil and bake in the heated oven for 20–30 minutes or until the fish flakes easily. Cooking time will depend on the thickness of the cod steaks.

450 g (1 lb) white fish
1 tablespoon flour
salt
a good shake of paprika
1 small red pepper, deseeded
   and thinly sliced
1 small green pepper, deseeded
   and thinly sliced
1 onion, sliced
100 g (4 oz) sweet corn
1 bay leaf
250 ml ($\frac{1}{2}$ pt) fish stock (recipe
   no. 45)

66

Casserole of fish

Set the oven at 180°C, 350°F or Gas No. 4.

Cut the fish into 4 cm (1$\frac{1}{2}$ in) squares.

Mix together the flour, salt and paprika and coat the fish in this mixture.

Place the fish, peppers, onion and sweet corn in layers in a casserole, add the bay leaf and pour over the fish stock.

Cover and bake in the heated oven for 45 minutes.

Serve from the casserole with potatoes and a green vegetable.

---

50 g (2 oz) margarine
50 g (2 oz) flour
500 ml (1 pt) soya milk
salt
2 tablespoons chopped parsley
450 g (1 lb) white fish fillets
100 g (4 oz) mushrooms, sliced
450 g (1 lb) potatoes, sliced 6
   mm ($\frac{1}{4}$ in) thick
a little oil or extra margarine

67

Saucy fish

Set the oven at 190°C, 375°F or Gas No. 5.

Grease a deep 2 litre (4 pt) casserole.

Melt the margarine in a saucepan, sprinkle in the flour, and cook for 2 minutes. Remove from the heat and stir in the soya milk a little at a time to make a smooth sauce. Return to the heat and cook until thickened. Season with a little salt and stir in the parsley.

Pour half this sauce into the bottom of the casserole and lay the fillets of fish on top of this sauce. Sprinkle over the mushrooms and then pour over the rest of the sauce.

Place the potato slices in cold salted water. Cover and bring to the boil, then simmer for 5 minutes.

Drain the potato slices and arrange them over the top of the casserole. Sprinkle over a little oil, or dot with margarine, and bake in the heated oven for 45–50 minutes.

---

225 g (8 oz) cod or haddock
   fillet
225 g (8 oz) smoked cod or
   haddock
1–2 small kipper fillets
250 ml ($\frac{1}{2}$ pt) soya milk
2 eggs
750 g (1$\frac{1}{2}$ lb) potatoes
75 g (3 oz) margarine
grated nutmeg
salt

68

25 g (1 oz) flour
2 tablespoons chopped parsley
a little extra margarine

Smoked fish pie

Set the oven at 190°C, 375°F or Gas No. 5.

Place the fish in an ovenproof dish. Pour over the soya milk, cover with foil and bake in the heated oven for 15–20 minutes, until the fish flakes easily.

Boil the eggs for 12 minutes. Cool under cold water. Peel, remove the yolks and discard. Chop the whites roughly.

Boil the potatoes for 20 minutes, drain and then mash them with 50 g (2 oz) of the margarine. Season with nutmeg and salt.

When the fish is cooked, pour off and reserve the liquid. Flake the fish and remove any skin and bones.

Use the reserved liquid to make the sauce. Place the rest of the margarine in a small saucepan. Sprinkle in the flour and cook for 30 seconds, then remove from the heat. Gradually add in the fish liquid. Return to the heat and boil until thick, then season.

To the sauce add the flaked fish, parsley and egg whites, and pour this mixture into a greased pie dish.

Top the pie with the mashed potato, dot with margarine and bake in the heated oven for 20–25 minutes until the top is nicely browned.

69

Trout and fennel parcels

1 bulb fennel
4 trout fillets
4 sheets filo pastry (recipe no. 189)
25 g (1 oz) margarine, melted

Set the oven to 190°C, 375°F or Gas No. 5.

First prepare the fennel. Remove any marked outside layers and cut off the top shoot and the bottom of the bulbous end. Cut the bulb crossways into thin slices.

Remove any skin from the trout fillets, starting at the tail end and pulling back sharply.

Place a sheet of filo pastry on the work surface and brush all over with margarine.

Lay the trout fillet on the pastry, skinned side up. Cover the trout with several layers of fennel slices. Parcel the fish in the pastry, tucking over the ends to seal the fish in.

Turn the parcels over and place them on a greased baking sheet. Brush all over with melted margarine and decorate with a strip of filo pastry.

Bake in the heated oven for 20 minutes until the pastry is golden-brown.

These are delicious served with stir-fried broccoli (recipe no. 142).

3
Main Meal Vegetable Dishes

List of Recipes

450 g (1 lb) button mushrooms
chopped chives or spring
  onions to garnish

For the batter
125 ml ($\frac{1}{4}$ pt) tepid water,
  43°C (110°F)
$\frac{1}{4}$ teaspoon sugar
$\frac{1}{4}$ teaspoon dried yeast
100 g (4 oz) flour
1 egg white
oil for frying

For the sauce
1 stick of celery, thinly sliced
1 carrot, thinly sliced
1 small red pepper, deseeded
  and thinly sliced
1 onion, thinly sliced
1 dessertspoon oil
250 ml ($\frac{1}{2}$ pt) chicken stock
  (recipe no. 1)
1 tablespoon soy sauce
1 tablespoon cornflour
2 tablespoons water

70

Changi mushrooms

Place the tepid water in a bowl and stir in the sugar. Sprinkle over the dried yeast and leave in a warm place for 5 minutes.

Sift the flour into a bowl, make a well in the centre, and add the yeast mixture. Stir until all the water and flour are mixed, beat until the batter is smooth, and put in a warm place for 30 minutes.

Remove the stalks from the mushrooms (the stalks can be used for soup). Wash and dry the caps and place on one side until needed.

To make the sauce, fry all the vegetables in the oil for 2 minutes only. Pour over the stock and the soy sauce and bring to the boil. Mix together the cornflour and the cold water. Add this to the sauce, stirring all the time, and cook until thickened. If needed, season with salt. Keep warm.

Now return to the batter. Whisk the egg white until stiff and fold into the batter.

Heat a pan of oil until very hot.

Dip the mushrooms into the batter and fry them in the oil until golden-brown and puffy; drain them on kitchen paper.

When ready to serve, pile the mushrooms on a heated dish and pour over the sauce. Sprinkle with chives or spring onions and serve with plain boiled rice (recipe no. 57).

---

4 tablespoons olive oil
1 onion, finely chopped
225 g (8 oz) mushrooms, sliced
1 stick of celery, chopped
2 tablespoons chopped parsley
125 ml ($\frac{1}{4}$ pt) chicken stock
  (recipe no. 1)

71

125 ml ($\frac{1}{4}$ pt) dry white wine
salt

Mushrooms with rice

100 g (4 oz) rice

Heat the oil in a saucepan and add the onion. Fry until the onion is golden-brown and then add the mushrooms. Stir well, cover the pan, and cook for 3 minutes.

Mix the celery into the mushroom mixture, together with the parsley, stock, wine and salt. Cover the pan and simmer very slowly for 15 minutes.

Stir in the rice and cook for a further 20 minutes until the rice is cooked and all the liquid absorbed.

Serve with a green salad (recipe no. 149).

50 g (2 oz) lentils
1 bay leaf
1 onion, chopped
225 g (8 oz) mushrooms,
  chopped
50 g (2 oz) fresh breadcrumbs
3 tablespoons chopped parsley
1 teaspoon dried thyme
salt
1 egg white
8 courgettes
250 ml ($\frac{1}{2}$ pt) chicken stock
  (recipe no. 1)
1 tablespoon oil
1 tablespoon cornflour
  (optional)
soy sauce (optional)

72

Stuffed courgettes

Set the oven at 190°C, 375°F or Gas No. 5.

Place the lentils in a pan of cold water and add the bay leaf. Cover the pan and simmer for 30 minutes, then drain.

Combine the onion, mushrooms, breadcrumbs, herbs and lentils and mix well. Season with a little salt and bind the mixture together with the egg white.

Peel the courgettes, cut in half lengthways and remove the seeds. Place them in a greased, deep ovenproof dish, keeping them in one layer.

Fill the centres of the courgettes with the stuffing and pour round the stock. Sprinkle the oil over the courgettes, cover with foil, and bake in the heated oven for 25 minutes, or until the courgettes are tender.

If a thick sauce is liked, pour off the stock into a small saucepan. Mix 1 tablespoon cornflour with a little water and add to the stock. Bring to the boil to thicken the sauce. Season with a little soy sauce, which will also improve the colour.

4 red or green peppers
2 tablespoons corn oil
1 stick of celery, finely chopped
1 carrot, finely chopped
100 g (4 oz) mushrooms,
  chopped
1 onion, finely chopped
100 g (4 oz) long-grain rice
1 dessertspoon yeast extract
250 ml (½ pt) water
salt to taste
½ teaspoon dried oregano
1 dessertspoon soy sauce
50 g (2 oz) flaked almonds
125 ml (¼ pt) chicken stock
  (recipe no. 1) or water

73

Stuffed peppers

To serve
4 slices of bread
oil for frying

Set the oven at 190°C, 375°F or Gas No. 5.

Cut the stalk end off the peppers and scoop out the white seeds from the inside. Bring some water to the boil and blanch the peppers for 3 minutes. Drain them upside down. Chop away the pepper from around the stalk and add it to the other vegetables.

Heat the oil in a saucepan, add all the vegetables, and cook for 5 minutes. Stir in the uncooked rice and cook for a further 2 minutes.

Dissolve the yeast extract in the boiling water and add this to the rice. Season with a little salt, oregano, and soy sauce. Cover the pan and simmer for about 15 minutes until the rice is tender and all the liquid absorbed. Stir in the flaked almonds.

Place the pepper cups in an oiled shallow ovenproof dish and fill them with the rice mixture. Pour round the chicken stock or water, cover the peppers with a lid or foil, and bake in the heated oven for 25–30 minutes until the peppers are tender. Do not overcook or the peppers will break.

Fry the slices of bread in the oil until crisp and brown. Drain the peppers and place one pepper on each slice. Serve with salad.

1 medium marrow
salt
2 tablespoons oil
1 small onion, chopped
225 g (8 oz) mushrooms,
  chopped
150 g (6 oz) wholemeal
  breadcrumbs
150 g (6 oz) ground mixed nuts
1 tablespoon chopped parsley
1 red pepper, deseeded and
  sliced into rings (optional)

74

Stuffed marrow rings

Set the oven at 180°C, 350°F or Gas No. 4.

Cut the marrow into 2.5 cm (1 in) slices and carefully remove the centre seeds. Blanch the marrow rings in boiling salted water for 2 minutes only. Remove from the pan, drain and place in a single layer in a greased ovenproof dish.

Heat the oil in a pan and fry the onion and mushrooms until soft. Add the breadcrumbs, mixed nuts and parsley. Season with a little salt and mix well.

Spoon the mixture into the centre of the marrow rings and place a ring of red pepper, if used, on each slice.

Bake in the heated oven for 20 minutes or until the marrow is tender.

Note: As a change, the marrow can be sliced in half lengthways and, after scooping out the centre, blanched for 5 minutes before filling with the same mixture and baking the same way.

450 g (1 lb) potatoes
salt
40 g (1½ oz) margarine
1 dessertspoon chopped chives
225 g (8 oz) cooked sweet corn
50 g (2 oz) flaked almonds
1 small red or green pepper,
  deseeded and diced

75

Potato pie

Set the oven at 190°C, 375°F or Gas No. 5.

Cook the potatoes in boiling salted water until tender; strain and mash well with 25 g (1 oz) of the margarine and the chives.

Grease a pie dish and place half the potato in the dish. Cover with a layer of sweet corn, almonds and pepper, and then cover with the rest of the potatoes. Fork the top into little peaks and dot with the rest of the margarine.

Bake in the heated oven for 30 minutes until the top is golden-brown.

Serve with a green salad (recipe no. 149).

Serves 2–3 people.

---

100 g (4 oz) mixed nuts (e.g. almonds, hazelnuts, walnuts)
225 g (8 oz) potatoes
salt to taste
¼ teaspoon dried basil or sage
1 tablespoon chopped parsley
1 egg white
fresh breadcrumbs
flour
oil for frying

76

Nut cutlets

Grind the nuts (a liquidizer does this very well) or chop them very finely.

Cook the potatoes in boiling salted water until tender. Drain them and reserve the water to make the sauce. Mash the potatoes.

Mix together the potato, ground or chopped nuts and herbs, and season with a little salt. Allow the mixture to cool, and form into cutlet shapes or round flat cakes.

Beat the egg white until it is well broken. Place in a flat dish, and spread the breadcrumbs on a plate.

Dip the shaped nut mixture into a little flour, then into the egg whites, and finally into the breadcrumbs. Press the coating on well and allow the coating to harden for about 10–15 minutes before frying.

Heat some oil in a frying pan and fry the cutlets until golden-brown (about 5–7 minutes each side).

Serve with an onion sauce made with the potato water (recipe no. 169) or mushroom sauce (recipe no. 92).

Serves 2–3 people.

75 g (3 oz) margarine
150 g (6 oz) plain flour
a pinch of salt
about 2 tablespoons cold water

Filling
450 g (1 lb) onions, thinly sliced
1 tablespoon olive oil
12 black olives
1 small tin of anchovy fillets,
    plus its oil
chopped fresh or dried
    rosemary

77

Onion flan

Set the oven at 200°C, 400°F or Gas No. 6.

Rub the margarine into the flour, with the salt, until the mixture resembles breadcrumbs, and add sufficient water to make a dough. Leave in the refrigerator for 30 minutes.

Fry the onions in the olive oil until soft and golden-brown. Allow to cool.

Remove the stones from the olives. Drain the anchovies from their oil, and keep the oil.

Roll out the pastry and line a 20 cm (8 in) flan tin.

Cover the base with the fried onions, and make a lattice over the top with the anchovy fillets. Place a black olive in each little square, and sprinkle the flan with rosemary. Pour over the oil from the can of anchovies and bake in the heated oven for 30–35 minutes.

This flan is best served warm, with a green salad (recipe no. 149).

100 g (4 oz) lentils
1 bay leaf
1 small onion, chopped
1 clove of garlic, crushed
2 tablespoons oil
1 large onion, sliced
1 small cauliflower
50 g (2 oz) green beans
salt
500 ml (1 pt) water
1 tablespoon soy sauce
    (optional)

78

Lentil and vegetable hotpot

Soak the lentils overnight, then simmer them gently with the bay leaf, the small chopped onion, and the garlic for about 30 minutes, until tender. Drain.

Heat the oil in a pan and fry the sliced large onion until soft and brown. Meanwhile, break the cauliflower into florets and cut the beans into 1 cm (½ in) pieces. Cook them both in boiling salted water until tender.

Mix the vegetables with the fried onions, then stir in the cooked lentils. Season with a little salt, if needed, and the soy sauce, if liked. Serve very hot.

---

100 g (4 oz) long-grain rice
1 onion, chopped
1 clove of garlic, crushed
2 tablespoons corn oil
1 green pepper, deseeded and
    chopped
225 g (8 oz) mushrooms,
    chopped
100 g (4 oz) mixed nuts,
    coarsely chopped
1 dessertspoon soy sauce
salt

79

Nutty rice

Cook the rice as directed in recipe no. 57 and leave on one side.

Cook the onion and garlic in the oil in a large frying pan until soft and golden-brown.

Add the pepper and mushrooms and fry for 2 further minutes.

Stir in the cooked rice, together with the nuts, and fry for 5 minutes.

Add the soy sauce and salt to taste. Serve really hot with a green salad (recipe no. 149).

450 g (1 lb) white cabbage,
  thinly sliced
1 medium onion, thinly sliced
salt
25 g (1 oz) margarine
75 g (3 oz) flaked almonds

For the sauce
25 g (1 oz) margarine
25 g (1 oz) flour
125 ml ($\frac{1}{4}$ pt) chicken stock
  (recipe no. 1) or soya milk
salt
grated nutmeg

80

Cabbage and almond bake

For the topping
browned breadcrumbs
15 g ($\frac{1}{2}$ oz) margarine

Set the oven at 220°C, 425°F or Gas No. 7.

Cook the cabbage and onion in boiling, salted water until just tender (about 8–10 minutes). Drain and reserve the liquid.

Melt 25 g (1 oz) margarine in a frying pan and fry the almonds until golden-brown. Sprinkle with salt.

To make the sauce, heat the margarine in a small saucepan and stir in the flour. Cook for 1 minute; remove from the heat and stir in the stock or soya milk, together with the same quantity of liquid from the cabbage. Return to the heat and cook until thick. Season with salt and nutmeg.

Grease a casserole with margarine or oil and place a layer of cooked cabbage in the bottom. Over this sprinkle half the browned almonds and cover with half of the sauce. Repeat the layers and sprinkle with the browned breadcrumbs. Dot with margarine and bake in the heated oven for 15 minutes.

Serves 2–3 as a main dish or 4 as a vegetable with slices of cold chicken breast.

100 g (4 oz) Patna rice
2 tablespoons oil
1 onion, chopped
25 g (1 oz) margarine
150 g (6 oz) frozen mixed
    vegetables
1 tablespoon soy sauce
a pinch of curry powder
salt to taste

81

Fried rice

Cook the rice as directed in recipe no. 57.

Heat the oil in a frying pan and fry the onion until soft and golden-brown. Stir in the cooked rice, add the margarine, and fry until the rice is really hot.

Cook the frozen vegetables according to the directions on the packet.

Add the cooked vegetables to the rice mixture. Turn up the heat and stir in the soy sauce and the curry powder. Add a little salt if necessary.

Serve with prawn crackers and a green salad (recipe no. 149).

Serves 2 people.

---

50 g (2 oz) margarine
50 g (2 oz) flour
325 g (12 oz) tin of sweet corn
the liquid from the tin of sweet
    corn made up to 250 ml
    ($\frac{1}{2}$ pt) with water
salt
grated nutmeg
4 egg whites

82

Sweet corn soufflé

Set the oven at 180°C, 350°F or Gas No. 4.

Melt the margarine in a small pan, stir in the flour, and cook for 2 minutes without browning. Remove from the heat and gradually add the sweet corn liquid, stirring all the time. Return the pan to the heat and cook until thick. Season with salt and a little nutmeg, and add the sweet corn.

Grease a 15 cm (6 in) soufflé dish.

Whisk the egg whites until they are stiff and dry, and fold them into the sweet corn mixture.

Pour the mixture into the soufflé dish and bake in the heated oven for 40 minutes until well-risen and golden-brown.

Serve immediately with a green salad (recipe no. 149).

Serves 2–3 people.

83

Mixed vegetables in batter

450 g (1 lb) mixed vegetables
(e.g. mushrooms, courgettes,
aubergine, cauliflower,
broccoli, french beans,
celery)
salt
flour
250 ml (½ pt) batter (recipe no.
84)
oil for deep-frying

Prepare the vegetables. Wash the mushrooms and leave whole if not too big, otherwise cut into bite-sized chunks.

Wash and slice the courgettes.

Slice the aubergine, sprinkle with salt and leave on one side for 10 minutes. (This draws the bitterness out of the flesh.) When ready, rinse and drain.

The other vegetables need to be cut into bite-sized pieces and then plunged into boiling salted water to cook for about 5 minutes. Remove and drain.

Dip all the vegetables into flour, then into the batter.

Deep-fry in batches in hot oil for 2–3 minutes until a crisp golden-brown. Drain on kitchen paper and serve with peanut sauce (recipe no. 168).

84

Batter

100 g (4 oz) white flour
a pinch of salt
25 g (1 oz) margarine, melted
125 ml (¼ pt) warm water
2 egg whites

Sift the flour into a bowl, make a well in the centre, add the salt and pour in the melted margarine and the warm water. Mix well with a fork and beat well until the mixture is smooth and bubbles rise to the surface. Leave on one side until it is completely cold (at least 20 minutes).

Whisk the egg whites until stiff and cut and fold them into the batter.

Use as required to coat small pieces of fish, vegetables or chicken.

Fry in very hot oil to give a crisp coating which stands away from the filling.

85

Vegetable stir-fry

100 g (4 oz) bean sprouts
50 g (2 oz) water chestnuts (optional)
1 red pepper
50 g (2 oz) mushrooms
50 g (2 oz) sweet corn (frozen or tinned)
2 tablespoons vegetable oil
soy sauce (optional)

Wash the bean sprouts and dry thoroughly; slice the water chestnuts thinly, if used; cut the pepper in half, discard the seeds and cut the flesh into long fine strips. Wash and slice the mushrooms, defrost the sweet corn kernels if frozen or drain if tinned.

Heat the oil in a frying pan or wok and when really hot add the vegetables. Keep them moving around the pan for 5–6 minutes.

A few drops of soy sauce can be added at the end of cooking, just before serving.

Note: Supermarkets now produce a frozen oriental vegetable mixture, which can be used in place of the fresh vegetables as a useful and unusual back-up.

225 g (8 oz) potatoes, cut into
1 cm (½ in) cubes
100 g (4 oz) carrots, cut into
julienne strips
100 g (4 oz) cauliflower, broken
into small florets
100 g (4 oz) cabbage, roughly
chopped
100 g (4 oz) courgettes or green
beans
50 g (2 oz) margarine
2 tablespoons chopped parsley
1 teaspoon dried basil
½ teaspoon salt

86

Roasted vegetables

Set the oven at 180°C, 350°F or Gas No. 4.

Place all the prepared vegetables in a casserole dish. Dot with the margarine and season with the herbs and salt.

Cover with a tight-fitting lid and bake in the heated oven for 30–40 minutes until the vegetables are tender and their delicious flavour has fully developed.

Serve with brown rice (recipe no. 36), pasta or mushroom sauce (recipe no. 92).

2 medium aubergines
1 tablespoon olive oil
1 small onion, chopped
1 clove of garlic, crushed
225 g (8 oz) mushrooms, finely
chopped
1 tablespoon chopped parsley
100 g (4 oz) wholemeal
breadcrumbs
25 g (1 oz) margarine

87

Stuffed aubergines

Set the oven at 180°C, 350°F or Gas No. 5.

Cut the aubergines in half, scoop out the flesh and chop it finely. Place the skin shells to one side for use later.

Heat the oil in a pan. Add the onion and garlic and fry for 1 minute.

Add the mushrooms, parsley and aubergine. Fry for 2–3 minutes. Stir in the breadcrumbs.

Fill the reserved aubergine shells with the stuffing mixture.

Dot with the margarine and bake in the heated oven for 30 minutes.

88

Spaghetti with aubergines

1 large aubergine
salt
2 tablespoons oil
1 medium onion, chopped
1 clove of garlic, crushed
1 red pepper, deseeded and
thinly sliced
125 ml ($\frac{1}{4}$ pt) vegetable or
chicken stock (recipe no. 1)
1 teaspoon dried oregano
225 g (8 oz) spaghetti

Slice the aubergine into 6 mm ($\frac{1}{4}$ in) slices, sprinkle with salt, and allow to stand for 30 minutes. (This will remove excess water and any bitter taste.)

Heat the oil in a large frying pan and fry the onion and garlic until soft and slightly brown. Pour off the liquid from the aubergine and pat the slices dry on kitchen paper. Add the prepared aubergine and the pepper rings to the frying pan and cook until the vegetables are soft and well mixed. Pour over the stock, season with a little salt, and sprinkle over the oregano. Cover the pan and simmer for 15 minutes.

Cook the spaghetti in plenty of boiling salted water for 12 minutes until just cooked. Drain and toss in a little oil. Arrange the spaghetti on a heated serving dish and pour the vegetable mixture into the middle.

Serves 2–3 people.

89

Fluffy baked potatoes

4 good-sized old potatoes
50 g (2 oz) margarine
1 small onion, finely chopped
$\frac{1}{2}$ teaspoon soy sauce
2 egg whites

Set the oven at 180°C, 350°F or Gas No. 4.

Scrub the potatoes, prick them with a fork, and bake in the heated oven for about 1$\frac{1}{2}$ hours.

When the potatoes are cooked, cut them in half and scoop the insides into a bowl.

Mix the margarine into the potato insides and add the onion. Season with a little soy sauce to taste.

Whisk the egg whites until they are stiff and carefully cut and fold them into the potato mixture. Place the mixture in the potato skins and return them to the oven to cook for a further 15 minutes.

Serve with salad.

---

4 large Spanish onions
salt
225 g (8 oz) minced chicken
  breast
flour
3 sage leaves, chopped
1 sprig of thyme, chopped
1 sprig of parsley, chopped
75 g (3 oz) margarine

90

Stuffed roast onion

Set the oven at 180°C, 350°F or Gas No. 4.

Peel and cut the root end off the onions. Cook the whole onions in a pan of boiling salted water for 15 minutes.

Drain the onions and scoop out most of the inside, using a pointed knife.

Chop half the scooped out onion and mix it with the minced chicken. Spoon the stuffing back into the onions and press the mixture in well, taking care not to break the onions. Place them in a greased baking dish; sprinkle with flour and the herbs. Place a knob of margarine on each onion and roast for 40 minutes.

Serve with plain boiled rice (recipe no. 57) and a green salad (recipe no. 149).

100 g (4 oz) lentils
salt
100 g (4 oz) ground mixed nuts
1 onion, finely chopped
1 clove of garlic, crushed
a pinch of dried sage
1 tablespoon chopped parsley
1 egg white
50 g (2 oz) fresh wholemeal
   breadcrumbs
oil for frying

91

Nut rissoles

Soak the lentils overnight. Drain and boil them in salted water until tender (about 30 minutes).

Drain them and reserve the liquid.

Mash the lentils well and add the ground mixed nuts. Add the onion, garlic, herbs and seasoning, and bind together with the egg white and a little of the reserved lentil liquid, if needed.

Shape into rissoles and roll them in the breadcrumbs. Fry in hot oil until golden-brown. Drain on kitchen paper and serve hot, with mushroom sauce (recipe no. 92).

25 g (1 oz) margarine or
   1 tablespoon oil
50 g (2 oz) mushrooms or
   mushroom stalks, finely
   chopped
25 g (1 oz) flour
250 ml (½ pt) vegetable water or
   stock
1 dessertspoon soy sauce
salt

92

Mushroom sauce

Melt the margarine or heat the oil in a small saucepan and add the mushrooms. Cook gently for about 10 minutes, but do not let the mushrooms get too brown.

Stir in the flour and cook for a further 2 minutes. Remove from the heat and gradually stir in the vegetable water or stock and the soy sauce. Bring back to the boil to thicken the sauce. Season with salt and serve with fritters (recipe no. 100), rissoles (recipe no. 91), nut cutlets (recipe no. 76) or vegetable stir-fry (recipe no. 85).

75 g (3 oz) wholemeal
  breadcrumbs
150 g (6 oz) ground mixed nuts
1 clove of garlic, crushed
1 teaspoon dried mixed herbs
100 ml (4 fl oz) oil
1 tablespoon oil
1 large onion, sliced
225 g (8 oz) mushrooms, sliced
25 g (1 oz) flour
125 ml ($\frac{1}{4}$ pt) stock
salt to taste

93

Mushroom crumble

Set the oven at 200°C, 400°F or Gas No. 6.

Mix together the breadcrumbs, ground mixed nuts, garlic and herbs. Pour over the oil and mix well. Leave on one side.

Heat the tablespoon of oil in a frying pan and fry the onion until soft and brown. Add the mushrooms and cook for a few minutes more. Sprinkle in the flour and cook for 2 minutes.

Remove from the heat and add the stock, stirring all the time. Return to the heat and cook until thick. Season to taste with a little salt.

Pour this mixture into the bottom of an ovenproof casserole and sprinkle over the crumble mixture.

Bake in the heated oven for 30 minutes.

Serve hot with vegetables and salad.

4
Chicken

List of Recipes

4 chicken breasts, boned and
  skinned
1 egg white
2 dessertspoons cornflour
salt
oil
450 g (1 lb) bean sprouts
1 green pepper, deseeded and
  thinly sliced
1 teaspoon sugar
1 teaspoon soy sauce

94

Chicken with bean sprouts

Cut the chicken breasts into long thin strips 6 mm ($\frac{1}{4}$ in) wide.

Beat the egg white lightly and add the cornflour and salt. Place the chicken strips in this mixture and mix well.

Heat 2 tablespoons of the oil in a large frying pan and, when really hot, add tablespoons of the chicken mixture to the pan. Stir around quickly to separate the pieces, and cook the chicken through. (This should not take more than 2–3 minutes, provided the chicken strips are cut thinly enough.) Drain the chicken pieces and keep them warm, and repeat with the rest of the chicken.

Add a little more oil to the frying pan if necessary. Heat and add the bean sprouts and the pepper. Cook for 1 minute, stirring all the time. Add salt to taste, the sugar and the soy sauce.

Mix the chicken and vegetables together and serve really hot with plain boiled rice (recipe no. 57).

4 chicken breasts, boned and
  skinned
2 tablespoons soy sauce
1 tablespoon dry white wine
1 teaspoon ground ginger
cornflour
4 tablespoons vegetable oil
100 g (4 oz) shredded almonds
2–3 spring onions, chopped

95

Marinated chicken with almonds

Cut the chicken breasts into 2.5 cm (1 in) squares and place in a dish.

Mix together the soy sauce, wine and ginger, and pour this over the chicken. Mix well and allow to marinate for 1–2 hours.

Drain the chicken from the marinade and coat each piece with cornflour.

In a frying pan heat the oil and, when hot, fry the pieces of chicken until golden-brown and cooked through. Drain and pile on a heated serving dish.

Slide the almonds into the oil and fry until golden-brown. Drain these and sprinkle over the chicken.

Garnish with the chopped spring onions.

---

4 chicken breasts, boned and
  skinned
1 large onion, sliced
1 bay leaf
1 blade of mace
grated nutmeg
250 ml ($\frac{1}{2}$ pt) water
250 ml ($\frac{1}{2}$ pt) soya milk
65 g (2$\frac{1}{2}$ oz) margarine
40 g (1$\frac{1}{2}$ oz) flour
salt
100 g (4 oz) button mushrooms

96

Chicken fricassée

Place the chicken breasts in a saucepan with the onion, bay leaf, blade of mace and some nutmeg. Mix together the water and soya milk and pour this over the chicken. Cover the pan, bring the liquid slowly to the boil, and simmer carefully for 35 minutes.

Remove the chicken from the pan and cut the flesh into neat cubes. Place them in an ovenproof dish and keep warm.

In a saucepan melt 40 g (1$\frac{1}{2}$ oz) of the margarine, stir in the flour, and cook for 2 minutes. Remove from the heat.

Strain the liquid from the chicken and pour this on to the flour and margarine, stirring all the time. Return to the heat to thicken. Season as necessary with a little salt, pour the sauce over the chicken and, again, keep warm.

Fry the mushrooms in the rest of the margarine until they are barely soft (about 2–3 minutes), and sprinkle them over the fricassée.

Note: When keeping this dish hot, take care that it does not over-heat, otherwise the chicken will shred and be unappetizing.

97

Spiced chicken

4 chicken breasts, skinned
1 onion, finely chopped
1 stick of celery, finely chopped
1 carrot, finely chopped
salt
1 bouquet garni (see page 242)
75 g (3 oz) margarine
¼ teaspoon turmeric
a good shake of cayenne
¾ teaspoon ground ginger
¼ teaspoon ground cumin

Place the chicken breasts in a pan. Cover with cold water and add all the vegetables. Season with a little salt and the bouquet garni. Cover the pan, bring to the boil, and simmer for 30 minutes. Allow the chicken to cool in the liquid.

Melt a third of the margarine in a small saucepan, add the spices and cook for 2–3 minutes to mellow the spices. Allow to go cold.

Cream the rest of the margarine and beat in the cold spiced margarine.

When the chicken is cold, remove from the liquid and place the breasts on an ovenproof serving dish, spread over the spiced margarine, and chill.

Heat the grill and place the chicken under it for about 6–8 minutes to brown the margarine.

Serve the dish cold with a rice and prawn salad (recipe no. 155).

98

Crunchy chicken bake

75 g (3 oz) margarine
50 g (2 oz) flour
250 ml (½ pt) chicken stock
  (recipe no. 1)
250 ml (½ pt) soya milk
4 chicken breasts, boned and
  skinned
100 g (4 oz) mushrooms, sliced
75 g (3 oz) flaked almonds
salt
50 g (2 oz) fresh breadcrumbs

Set the oven at 200°C, 400°F or Gas No. 6.

Melt 50 g (2 oz) of the margarine in a saucepan. Add the flour and cook for 2 minutes. Remove from the heat and gradually add the stock and soya milk mixed together. Bring the mixture to the boil and cook until thick.

Cut each chicken breast into 4 pieces.

Grease a 1.7 litre (3 pt) casserole and place in the pieces of chicken breast and the sliced mushrooms. Sprinkle with the almonds and season with a little salt. Pour over the sauce.

Melt the rest of the margarine in a small frying pan, add the breadcrumbs and fry until golden-brown.

Sprinkle the crumbs over the casserole and bake for 40 minutes in the heated oven.

---

flour
a pinch of salt
½ teaspoon dried oregano
4 chicken breasts, boned and
   skinned
2 egg whites
50 g (2 oz) browned
   breadcrumbs
oil for frying
corn fritters to serve (recipe no. 100)

99

Chicken Maryland

Mix the flour with a pinch of salt and the oregano.

Dip the chicken breasts in the seasoned flour and brush off any excess.

Beat the egg whites until well broken, and place the breadcrumbs on a flat plate.

Dip the floured breasts first in the egg white, then in the breadcrumbs, pressing them on well to give a good coating.

Heat some oil in a frying pan, about 1 cm (½ in) deep, and fry the breasts until they are cooked through. Start off with a high heat to brown the meat, then reduce the heat and cook for 6–8 minutes each side.

Drain the chicken breasts on kitchen paper and serve with corn fritters and a green vegetable or salad.

100 g (4 oz) plain flour
2 teaspoons soya flour
2 egg whites
a pinch of salt
325 g (12 oz) tin of sweet corn
4 tablespoons liquid from the
   tin of sweet corn
corn oil for frying

100

Corn fritters

Sift the plain flour and the soya flour together in a bowl, make a well in the centre, and add the egg whites, together with the salt and 1–2 tablespoons of the sweet corn liquid. Mix to a smooth batter and beat well.

Add the rest of the sweet corn liquid, and leave the batter to stand for 10 minutes.

Heat a thin layer of corn oil in a frying pan.

Add the sweet corn to the batter and drop spoonfuls of the batter into the hot oil. Fry the fritters on both sides until golden-brown and puffy. Drain on kitchen paper and serve hot.

Note: Tinned artichoke hearts, tinned asparagus or whole mushrooms can be used instead of sweet corn.

4 chicken breasts, boned and
   skinned
flour
salt
grated nutmeg
25 g (1 oz) margarine
1 tablespoon corn oil
125 ml ($\frac{1}{4}$ pt) dry white wine
125 ml ($\frac{1}{4}$ pt) chicken stock
   (recipe no. 1)
12 sage leaves, coarsely
   chopped

101

Sage chicken breasts

Dip the chicken breasts in the flour, which has been seasoned with salt and a little nutmeg.

Heat the margarine and oil in a frying pan and sauté the chicken breasts until golden-brown on both sides. Pour over the wine and stock and add the sage.

Cover the pan with a lid or plate and simmer the chicken for 20 minutes.

Remove the chicken breasts and place them on a heated serving dish to keep them warm. Bring the remaining liquid in the frying pan to the boil and boil rapidly until well-reduced (about half the quantity).

Strain the sauce over the chicken breasts and serve hot.

102

Chicken Antony

4 chicken breasts, boned and skinned
1 tablespoon oil
50 g (2 oz) margarine
1 clove of garlic, crushed
1 onion, sliced
25 g (1 oz) flour
250 ml (½ pt) chicken stock (recipe no. 1)
1 bouquet garni (see page 242)
salt
100 g (4 oz) mushrooms, chopped

Sauté the chicken breasts in the oil and half of the margarine until they are brown and sealed, then remove them from the pan.

Put the garlic and onion into the pan; brown them in the juices and oil and sprinkle in the flour. Cook for 1 minute and remove from the heat. Gradually add in the stock. Return to the heat and cook until thickened.

Replace the chicken in the pan and add the bouquet garni and season. Cover and simmer for 30–35 minutes.

Meanwhile, melt the rest of the margarine in a small pan and cook the mushrooms for about 2 minutes.

When the chicken is done, remove the bouquet garni and add the mushrooms to the sauce.

Serve hot with mashed potatoes and a green vegetable.

103

Chinese fried chicken

4 chicken breasts, boned and
  skinned
6 tablespoons soy sauce
4 tablespoons white wine
½ teaspoon sugar
a little flour
oil for frying
2 spring onions, chopped, to
  garnish

Cut the chicken into bite-sized pieces and marinate in the soy sauce,
wine and sugar mixed together. Leave for at least 1 hour.

Remove the chicken from the marinade and dip each piece in flour.

Heat some oil in a frying pan and fry the pieces of chicken until
golden-brown; this should take about 5 minutes.

Serve the chicken on a bed of plain boiled rice (recipe no. 57),
garnished with spring onions.

Heat the rest of the marinade and serve separately.

104

Cerney chicken casserole

4 chicken breasts, boned and
  skinned
1 onion, chopped
1 carrot, chopped
1 bouquet garni (see page 242)
salt
50 g (2 oz) margarine
50 g (2 oz) flour
500 ml (1 pt) stock from the
  chicken
100 g (4 oz) mushrooms, sliced
75 g (3 oz) almonds, flaked
300 g (12 oz) tin of asparagus
  spears

For the topping
2 tablespoons oil
50 g (2 oz) fresh breadcrumbs

Set the oven at 180°C, 350°F or Gas No. 4.

Place the chicken breasts in a saucepan, cover with cold water, and
add the onion, carrot and bouquet garni. Season with a little salt.

Cover the pan and bring to the boil. Simmer gently for 30 minutes. Remove the chicken breasts, strain the stock and reserve.

Melt the margarine in a saucepan and add the flour. Cook for 2 minutes, then remove from the heat. Gradually add the stock. Return to the heat and cook until thick.

Cut the chicken breasts into neat pieces. Add the chicken, mushrooms and almonds to the sauce.

Grease a 1.7 litre (3 pt) casserole.

Place half the chicken mixture in the casserole, and arrange the drained asparagus spears over the top. Cover with the rest of the chicken mixture.

To make the topping, heat the oil in a small saucepan and add the breadcrumbs. Fry until golden-brown and sprinkle over the casserole.

Bake in the heated oven for 40 minutes.

105

Leekie chicken

4 chicken breasts
40 g (1½ oz) wholemeal flour
salt
2 tablespoons oil
1 large carrot, sliced
2 large leeks, cut into 6 mm (¼ in) slices
375 ml (⅔ pt) chicken stock (recipe no. 1)

Set the oven at 180°C, 350°F or Gas No. 4.

Coat the chicken pieces with the flour mixed with a little salt. Brush off any excess.

Heat the oil in a saucepan and fry the chicken pieces until golden-brown but not cooked through. Remove them from the pan and place on one side.

Add the vegetables to the pan and fry them over a low heat until soft. Sprinkle in the flour remaining from coating the chicken and cook this with the vegetables for 2 minutes. Remove from the heat and gradually stir in the stock. Return to the heat and stir until thickened.

Place the chicken pieces in the saucepan, stir well, then cover the pan and allow to simmer for 35 minutes. Stir two or three times during cooking to prevent sticking. If cooking the dish as a casserole, leave it in the heated oven for 50 minutes.

1.5 kg (3 lb) roasting chicken
salt
2 sprigs of rosemary
50 g (2 oz) margarine
250 ml ($\frac{1}{2}$ pt) chicken stock
(recipe no. 1)
125 ml ($\frac{1}{4}$ pt) dry white wine
(optional)
1 dessertspoon cornflour

106

Roast chicken

Set the oven at 190°C, 375°F or Gas No. 5.

Wipe the inside of the chicken, season it with salt, and place the sprigs of rosemary inside. Rub the margarine over the breast of the bird.

Set the chicken in a roasting tin and pour round the stock and wine, if used.

Roast in the heated oven for 1 hour, basting every 15 minutes. Test to see that the juices from the chicken are clear.

When cooked remove the chicken to a heated serving dish.

Mix the cornflour with a little water, bring the liquid in the roasting tin to the boil, and stir in the cornflour. Bring back to the boil and simmer for 2 minutes, or longer if the gravy seems too thin. If necessary, season with a little salt and serve separately.

Serve with bread sauce (recipe no. 107) and stuffing balls (recipe no. 108).

2 cloves
1 small onion
250 ml ($\frac{1}{2}$ pt) water or soya milk
1 blade of mace
100 g (4 oz) stale breadcrumbs
15 g ($\frac{1}{2}$ oz) margarine
salt

107

Bread sauce

Press the cloves into the onion and place in a small saucepan with the water or soya milk.

Bring to the boil, add the mace and the breadcrumbs, and stand in a hot place to infuse for 30 minutes. Do *not* let the mixture boil.

Remove the onion, cloves and mace; beat in the margarine and salt to taste.

Reheat and serve with roast chicken (recipe no. 106).

108

Stuffing balls

50 g (2 oz) margarine
1 shallot, finely chopped
100 g (4 oz) fresh breadcrumbs
2 tablespoons chopped parsley
1 teaspoon dried thyme
½ teaspoon salt
1 egg white
a little vegetable oil

Melt the margarine in a small pan and fry the shallot until soft and transparent.

Remove from the heat and add the breadcrumbs and herbs. Season with salt to taste, then bind the mixture together with the egg white.

When cool enough to handle, mould the stuffing into small balls.

Brush the stuffing balls with a little vegetable oil. Place in the roasting pan along with the chicken (recipe no. 106) and cook in the oven for 15 minutes.

109

Chicken with chestnuts

4 chicken breasts, boned and skinned
3 tablespoons oil
1 onion, sliced
125 ml (¼ pt) stock or liquid from the tin of chestnuts made up with water
6 tablespoons soy sauce
6 tablespoons white wine
1 dessertspoon caster sugar
325 g (12 oz) tin of chestnuts

Cut each chicken breast into 6 pieces.

Heat the oil in a deep frying pan and fry the onion for 2 minutes. Add the chicken pieces and sauté quickly for 6 minutes.

Add the stock to the pan, together with the soy sauce. Cover the pan with a lid and simmer for 30 minutes, taking care that the liquid does not evaporate completely.

After this time, add the wine and the sugar, stir well, and cook for a further 10 minutes.

Add the drained chestnuts, and heat through.

Serve with plain boiled rice (recipe no. 57) and a green salad.

Note: Fresh chestnuts can be used in this recipe. Prepare them (as in recipe no. 137), then cook them in stock or water for 15 minutes.

110

Chicken in walnut sauce

50 g (2 oz) margarine
4 chicken breasts
125 ml (¼ pt) dry white wine
2 tablespoons stock or water
50 g (2 oz) ground walnuts
salt
chopped parsley to garnish

Melt the margarine in a frying pan and brown the chicken breasts. Pour over the wine and stock or water, cover the pan and simmer gently for about 25–30 minutes until the chicken breasts are tender. If the pan gets too dry, add a little extra stock or water.

When cooked, place the chicken on a serving dish.

Bring the juices in the frying pan to the boil and add the ground walnuts. Add a pinch of salt and boil for 1–2 minutes. Pour the sauce over the chicken and garnish with chopped parsley.

111

Chicken stir-fry

2 chicken breasts, boned and skinned
1 dessertspoon soy sauce
1 teaspoon garlic and ginger paste (recipe no. 112)
2 teaspoons oil
50 g (2 oz) mushrooms, thinly sliced
1 stick of celery, thinly sliced
75 g (3 oz) green, red or yellow pepper, deseeded and thinly sliced
1 medium onion, thinly sliced
1 small carrot, thinly sliced

Cut the chicken breasts into strips.

Place the chicken strips in a bowl. Add the soy sauce and the garlic and ginger paste. Mix well and leave on one side.

Heat the oil in a large frying pan or wok and add all the vegetables. Stir-fry quickly for 30 seconds.

Add the chicken breasts together with any soy sauce left in the bowl. Continue to stir-fry until the chicken is cooked – about 2–3 minutes.

Serve immediately with plain boiled rice (recipe no. 57).

112

Garlic and ginger paste

100 g (4 oz) fresh ginger root, peeled
50 g (2 oz) cloves of garlic, peeled
½ teaspoon salt
2 tablespoons soya oil

Finely grate the ginger into a small bowl.

Crush the garlic with the salt and add to the ginger.

Mix well and stir in the oil.

Note: This mixture will fill an empty mustard jar and will keep in the refrigerator.

If you have a liquidizer the whole process can be speeded up by putting the oil into the goblet with the salt and then dropping the garlic cloves and small pieces of root ginger on to the spinning blades.

This paste is very versatile and can be used in vegetable or chicken dishes or even as part of a salad dressing.

113

Chicken satay

2 chicken breasts, boned and skinned
50 g (2 oz) crunchy peanut butter
4 tablespoons water or chicken stock
2 tablespoons soy sauce
1 teaspoon grated fresh ginger root
2 tablespoons honey
1 clove of garlic, crushed
1 small onion, finely chopped
2 teaspoons mild curry powder
1 teaspoon ground cumin
1 teaspoon ground coriander

Cut the chicken breasts into strips 2.5 cm (1 in) wide, 6 mm (¼ in) thick and 8–10 cm (3–4 in) long.

Combine all the other ingredients in a shallow bowl to make a peanut sauce/marinade.

Add the chicken strips to the sauce, ensuring that each is well and truly coated and then marinade for several hours in the refrigerator.

Remove the chicken from the peanut mixture and thread each strip lengthways on a skewer.

Heat the grill or barbecue and cook the chicken skewers for about 3 minutes on each side. Do not overcook or the meat will become hard.

Heat the peanut sauce and serve as a dip or as a dressing for the chicken satay.

5
New Protein Dishes

List of Recipes

114

To reconstitute TVP

Allow 25 g (1 oz) dried TVP per person.

To soak TVP, use chicken stock (recipe no. 1) or yeast extract stock made from 1 teaspoon yeast extract for each 250 ml ($\frac{1}{2}$ pt) water. Dissolve the yeast extract in boiling water.

100 g (4 oz) TVP needs to be soaked in 500 ml (1 pt) stock.

Minimum times for soaking TVP: mince – 5–6 minutes; flakes – 15–20 minutes; chunks – 25–30 minutes; large pieces – 1–2 hours.

These are minimum times. TVP can be left to soak for longer, even overnight.

115

Country casserole

2 teaspoons yeast extract
500 ml (1 pt) water
100 g (4 oz) TVP chunks
50 g (2 oz) lentils
2 tablespoons oil
1 large onion, sliced
1 clove of garlic, crushed
1 red pepper, deseeded and
    sliced
1 green pepper, deseeded and
    sliced
2 tablespoons flour
1 bouquet garni (see page 242)

Set the oven at 160°C, 325°F or Gas No. 3.

Dissolve the yeast extract in the boiling water and pour over the TVP chunks and the lentils. Allow to soak for 2–3 hours or overnight.

Heat the oil in a frying pan and fry the onion and garlic until soft. Remove from the frying pan and place half the onion mixture in the bottom of a casserole.

Drain the TVP and the lentils and reserve the stock in which they were soaked. Add the TVP and lentils to the frying pan and fry for 5 minutes.

Layer the casserole with TVP and lentils, peppers and onion, finishing with a layer of TVP and lentils.

Add the flour to any oil left in the frying pan; add a little extra oil if all the oil has been absorbed, and stir over the heat for 2 minutes. Remove from the heat and stir in the reserved stock, a little at a time, to make a smooth gravy.

Pour this over the casserole, add the bouquet garni, cover and cook in the heated oven for 2½–3 hours.

Alternatively, this can be cooked in a crock-pot or slow cooker. Follow the maker's instructions to heat up the pot first, layer the TVP and vegetables as in the recipe, and cook for 6 hours, or longer.

---

1 teaspoon yeast extract
500 ml (1 pt) water
100 g (4 oz) TVP chunks
1 tablespoon oil
2 large carrots, chopped
1 leek, chopped
1 large onion, chopped
2 sticks of celery, chopped
50 g (2 oz) Patna or long grain rice
1 teaspoon soy sauce

116

Hinton hotpot

Set the oven at 180°C, 350°F or Gas No. 4.

Dissolve the yeast extract in the boiling water and pour over the TVP. Leave to soak for 1 hour or longer.

Heat the oil in a saucepan and fry the vegetables until they are soft and golden-brown. Add the rice and cook for 3 further minutes.

Strain the TVP from the liquid. Add the chunks to the vegetables and cook for a few moments to brown the TVP a little.

Add the liquid left from the soaked TVP, and add the soy sauce.

Cook the hotpot in a casserole in the heated oven for 1½ hours, or alternatively cover and simmer for 1 hour on top of the cooker.

Serve with herb dumplings (recipe no. 117).

117

Herb dumplings

100 g (4 oz) plain flour
salt
1 teaspoon baking powder
50 g (2 oz) margarine
1 teaspoon dried mixed herbs
100 ml (4 fl oz) water

Sift the flour with the salt and baking powder. Rub the margarine into the flour until the mixture resembles breadcrumbs.

Mix in the herbs and add the water to make a very soft dough.

Remove the lid from the casserole or saucepan 30 minutes before the end of the cooking time (recipe no. 116), and place small balls of the mixture on top of the vegetables. Replace the lid and cook for a further 30 minutes.

118

Leekie pie

100 g (4 oz) flaked TVP
500 ml (1 pt) chicken stock
  (recipe no. 1)
3 large leeks
reserved chicken stock made
  up to 250 ml (½ pt) with extra
  stock or water
25 g (1 oz) margarine
25 g (1 oz) flour
salt
grated nutmeg
1 quantity wholemeal pastry
  (recipe no. 187)

Set the oven at 200°C, 400°F or Gas No. 6.

Soak the flaked TVP in well-flavoured chicken stock for 20 minutes or longer.

Remove the root end from the leeks and cut off the green top to within 2.5 cm (1 in) of the white and discard. Cut the rest of the leeks into slices 2.5 cm (1 in) thick and wash thoroughly.

Grease a 1 litre (2 pt) pie dish, and drain the TVP from any chicken stock that may be left unabsorbed. Make this up to 250 ml (½ pt) with water or extra chicken stock and place on one side.

Place the leeks and the TVP in layers in the pie dish.

In a small saucepan, melt the margarine, add the flour and cook for

2 minutes. Remove from the heat, and add the reserved 250 ml ($\frac{1}{2}$ pt) chicken stock a little at a time, stirring well between each addition. Return to the heat and cook until thick.

Season the sauce with a little salt and nutmeg and pour over the leeks and TVP in the pie dish.

Cover the pie with wholemeal pastry and bake in the heated oven for 30 minutes, then reduce the heat to 180°C, 350°F or Gas No. 4 and cook for a further 15 minutes.

119

Roger's rissoles

1 teaspoon yeast extract
125 ml ($\frac{1}{4}$ pt) water
100 g (4 oz) TVP mince
450 g (1 lb) potatoes
1 medium onion, finely chopped
1 clove of garlic, crushed
  (optional)
1 teaspoon dried mixed herbs
salt
flour
oil

Dissolve the yeast extract in the boiling water, pour over the TVP mince and set on one side until needed.

Cook the potatoes.

Mash the potatoes and place in a large mixing bowl. Drain the TVP and add with the onion to the potatoes. Add the garlic, if used, and the herbs and season with a little salt. Mix very well.

Divide the mixture into 8 and shape each piece into a round about 7.5 cm (3 in) in diameter.

Dip the rissoles in the flour and brush off any excess.

Fry the rissoles in hot oil for 6 minutes on each side until golden-brown, then drain on kitchen paper. Serve with a sauce such as onion sauce (recipe no. 169), made with the liquid left over from soaking the TVP.

2 teaspoons yeast extract
250 ml (½ pt) water
100 g (4 oz) TVP mince
25 g (1 oz) margarine
1 tablespoon oil
2 onions, finely chopped
2 carrots, finely chopped
100 g (4 oz) mushrooms,
    chopped
a little dry white wine
    (optional)
salt
1 bay leaf

120

Spaghetti tevenaise

Dissolve the yeast extract in the boiling water and pour over the TVP mince. Leave to soak for 10 minutes or longer.

Heat the margarine and oil in a saucepan and add all the vegetables. Fry until the vegetables are soft and golden-brown.

Drain the TVP mince from the stock and add the mince to the vegetables. Fry for 5 minutes to brown the TVP.

Add enough of the liquid from the soaked TVP just to cover the contents of the saucepan, together with a little wine, if used. Season with salt and add the bay leaf. Cover the pan and simmer for 40 minutes until reduced and slightly thickened.

To serve
salt
325 g (12 oz) spaghetti
a little oil

Bring a large pan of salted water to the boil and add the spaghetti. Stir well, and allow to cook for 12 minutes until the spaghetti is cooked, but still firm. Drain from the water and toss in a little oil.

Pile the spaghetti on a heated serving dish and pour the tevenaise sauce in the centre.

Serve with a green salad (recipe no. 149).

2 large aubergines or 1 large
   aubergine and 1 large potato,
   sliced
salt
1 teaspoon yeast extract
250 ml (½ pt) water
100 g (4 oz) TVP mince
oil for frying
2 onions, chopped
100 g (4 oz) mushrooms,
   chopped
1 clove of garlic, crushed
2 tablespoons chopped parsley

For the sauce
25 g (1 oz) margarine
25 g (1 oz) flour
275 ml (½ pt) soya milk
salt
grated nutmeg

121

Moussaka

For the topping
browned breadcrumbs
15 g (½ oz) margarine

Set the oven at 190°C, 375°F or Gas No. 5.

Sprinkle the aubergine slices with salt and leave on one side for 30 minutes.

Dissolve the yeast extract in the boiling water and pour over the TVP mince. Leave to soak for 10 minutes or longer.

Heat the oil in a pan and fry the onions, mushrooms and garlic until they are soft and browned. Add the drained TVP and cook for 2 further minutes. Pour in enough of the yeast extract stock just to cover the contents of the saucepan; add the parsley and season with salt. Cover and simmer for 10 minutes. Drain off the liquid made by the aubergines and pat the slices dry on kitchen paper. Fry the aubergine and potato slices if used, in some oil until golden-brown.

To make the sauce, melt the margarine in a small pan and stir in the flour. Cook for 2 minutes and remove from the heat. Stir in the soya milk, return to the heat, and cook until thick. Season with salt and nutmeg.

Grease a casserole and place a third of the aubergine in the bottom. Cover with a layer of half the TVP mixture and cover that with another third of the aubergine. Add the rest of the TVP mixture, and finally cover this with the last of the aubergine. Pour over the sauce, and sprinkle the top with browned breadcrumbs. Dot the top with a little margarine and bake in the heated oven for 40 minutes.

Serve with a green salad (recipe no. 149).

Serves 4–6 people.

122

Tamburgers

2 teaspoons yeast extract
125 ml (¼ pt) water
100 g (4 oz) TVP mince
100 g (4 oz) fresh breadcrumbs
salt
1 teaspoon dried mixed herbs
1 egg white
flour
oil for frying

Dissolve the yeast extract in the boiling water and pour over the TVP mince. Allow to stand for 5–10 minutes.

Drain the TVP mince (save any of the liquid and use this to make a sauce).

Place the mince in a bowl and stir in the breadcrumbs, salt to taste, and herbs. Add the egg white and mix well until the mixture binds together. Shape the mixture firmly into 8 round flat cakes.

Dip the shaped patties in flour, brush off any excess, and fry them in hot oil for 5–7 minutes each side. Drain on kitchen paper and serve hot.

Serving suggestions
Serve as a main meal with a green vegetable, potatoes, and a sauce or gravy.

Serve as a snack with salad, or use the patties as a filling for a bread roll.

Note: These patties can be made in larger quantities and frozen uncooked until required. Fry the frozen patties for about 8–10 minutes on each side.

100 g (4 oz) flaked TVP
500 ml (1 pt) chicken stock
   (recipe no. 1)
2 medium onions, sliced
2 tablespoons corn oil
225 g (8 oz) mushrooms, sliced
1 tablespoon cornflour
3 teaspoons water
salt

For the pastry
150 g (6 oz) wholemeal flour
50 g (2 oz) soya flour
100 g (4 oz) margarine
about 2 tablespoons cold water

123

Harvest pie

Set the oven at 200°C, 400°F or Gas No. 6.

To make the pastry, mix together the flours and rub in the margarine until the mixture resembles breadcrumbs. Add the water and mix to a soft dough. Knead lightly.

As this pastry is very short and crumbly, it is best to leave it covered in a refrigerator for about 30 minutes before rolling out.

Soak the flaked TVP in the chicken stock for at least 20 minutes or longer.

Fry the onions in the oil until soft, add the mushrooms and cook for a further 4 minutes.

Drain the TVP from the stock and reserve this liquid.

Add the drained TVP to the onion mixture and cook for 5 minutes.

Pour over enough of the reserved stock to barely cover the TVP and vegetables.

Mix together the cornflour and water and add this to the pan. Bring to the boil, stirring all the time, to thicken the mixture. Season with a little salt, cover and simmer for 5 minutes. Pour the mixture into a 1 litre (2 pt) pie dish. Allow to cool.

Cover with the pastry and bake in the heated oven for 30 minutes.

124

Crunchy soy

1 dessertspoon yeast extract
250 ml (½ pt) water
100 g (4 oz) TVP slices
oil for frying

Dissolve the yeast extract in the boiling water and pour over the TVP slices. Allow to stand for 20–30 minutes or longer.

Drain the slices and fry them in hot oil until golden-brown. Drain on kitchen paper and serve.

Serve as a snack with a sauce made from peanuts (recipe no. 168) or as a main meal, served with an onion sauce (recipe no. 169), potatoes and a green vegetable.

Note: These slices of TVP can also be soaked in chicken stock or a vegetable juice, then fried as above.

125

Singapore special

3 tablespoons soy sauce
3 tablespoons peanut oil
1 large onion, finely chopped
1 tablespoon grated fresh ginger
    root or 1 teaspoon ground
    ginger
6 coriander seeds, crushed
a pinch of cumin
a pinch of curry powder

Mix all the ingredients together.

Dip slices of soaked TVP in the mixture before deep-frying, to make crunchy soy (recipe no. 124), or use to brush over chicken breasts before grilling.

1 teaspoon yeast extract
250 ml ($\frac{1}{2}$ pt) water
100 g (4 oz) TVP mince
450 g (1 lb) potatoes
1 large onion, chopped
1 clove of garlic, crushed
(optional)
1 tablespoon oil
1 tablespoon chopped parsley
1 tablespoon chopped chives
a pinch of dried thyme
salt
15 g ($\frac{1}{2}$ oz) margarine

126

Crofter's pie

Set the oven at 180°C, 350°F or Gas No. 4.

Dissolve the yeast extract in the boiling water and pour over the TVP mince (see recipe no. 114). Leave on one side until needed.

Boil the potatoes until tender; drain and mash.

Fry the onion and garlic, if used, in the oil until soft and browned, then add the drained soaked TVP mince. Add the herbs and salt and mix well.

Pour this mixture into a pie dish and cover with the mashed potatoes. Dot the top with a little margarine and bake in the heated oven for 30–40 minutes until the top is golden-brown.

100 g (4 oz) TVP chunks
1 teaspoon yeast extract
500 ml (1 pt) water
1 tablespoon oil
1 medium onion, sliced
2 medium carrots, sliced
50 g (2 oz) mushrooms, sliced
1 clove of garlic, crushed
25 g (1 oz) flour
$\frac{1}{2}$ teaspoon dried oregano
salt

127

Chunky stew

Place the TVP chunks in a bowl. Dissolve the yeast extract in the boiling water and pour this over the chunks. Allow to stand for 2–3 hours or overnight.

Heat the oil in a pan, add the vegetables and garlic and fry for 10 minutes, or until the vegetables are soft and golden-brown.

Drain the TVP and reserve the liquid.

Add the TVP to the vegetables in the pan and fry for a further 5 minutes.

Stir in the flour and cook for a further 2 minutes.

Remove from the heat and add the liquid from the soaked TVP, a little at a time, stirring between each addition.

Return the pan to the heat and stir until thickened. Lower the heat and sprinkle in the oregano and a little salt to taste. Simmer for 20 minutes and serve with potatoes and a green vegetable or salad.

128

Garlic slices

2 teaspoons yeast extract
325 ml (½ pt) water
100 g (4 oz) TVP slices
50 g (2 oz) wholemeal flour
1 teaspoon dried thyme
2 tablespoons oil
2 tablespoons chopped parsley
1 clove of garlic, crushed
1 tablespoon soy sauce

Set the oven at 190°C, 375°F or Gas No. 5.

Dissolve the yeast extract in the boiling water and pour this over the TVP slices. Leave to soak for 2–3 hours or overnight.

Drain the slices and reserve the liquid.

Mix together the flour and the thyme. Heat the oil in a frying pan.

Dip the TVP slices in the seasoned flour. Fry them in the oil until golden-brown, and place them in a casserole. Sprinkle each layer of slices with parsley.

Fry the garlic in the remaining oil in the frying pan and then add any flour left over from coating the slices. Stir until browned. Remove from the heat and stir in the reserved liquid, a little at a time. Return to the heat and cook until thick.

Add the soy sauce and pour the sauce over the slices in the casserole.

Cover the casserole and cook in the heated oven for 1½ hours.

Serve with potatoes and a green vegetable.

1 teaspoon yeast extract
250 ml (½ pt) water
100 g (4 oz) TVP mince
100 g (4 oz) macaroni
salt
1 onion, finely chopped
1 red pepper, deseeded and
    finely chopped
1 tablespoon oil
1 tablespoon chopped mint

For the sauce
250 ml (½ pt) soya milk
2 cloves
1 small onion
25 g (1 oz) margarine
25 g (1 oz) flour

129

Macaroni surprise

Set the oven at 190°C, 375°F or Gas No. 5.

Place the soya milk for the sauce in a small saucepan. Stick the cloves into the small onion and place this in the milk. Bring to the boil, and leave it on one side in a warm place to flavour the milk.

Dissolve the yeast extract in the boiling water and pour over the TVP mince. Leave for 10 minutes.

Cook the macaroni in boiling salted water until just cooked (about 12 minutes). Drain, rinse and leave until needed.

Fry the chopped onion and pepper in the oil. Drain the TVP mince and add to the vegetables. Season with salt and mint, and cook slowly for 10 minutes.

To make the sauce, melt the margarine in a small saucepan, and stir in the flour. Remove from the heat and add the strained, flavoured milk. Return to the heat and cook until thickened.

Grease a casserole and place half the macaroni in the bottom. Cover with half the sauce, and pour in all the TVP mixture. Top this with the rest of the macaroni and, finally, cover with the rest of the sauce.

Bake in the heated oven for 30 minutes.

Serve with salad and bread.

Note: This dish can be prepared some time in advance, and it also freezes very well.

150 g (6 oz) Quorn (see page 20)
2 cloves of garlic, crushed
2 teaspoons grated fresh ginger
   root
1 tablespoon soy sauce
1 carrot, sliced into thick
   matchsticks
½ green pepper, deseeded and
   cut into fine strips
½ red pepper, deseeded and cut
   into fine strips
1 onion, thinly sliced
2 sticks of celery, thinly sliced
2 tablespoons vegetable oil

130

Quickie stir-fry

Cut the Quorn chunks into 2 or 3 slices. Place them in a bowl and add the garlic, ginger and soy sauce. Leave on one side to marinate while preparing the vegetables.

Heat the oil in a frying pan or wok to a high heat and add the vegetables. Stir well to coat them with oil. Add the Quorn and the marinade. Continue to stir-fry for 5 minutes.

Serve immediately, with plain boiled rice (recipe no. 57).

25 g (1 oz) margarine
1 medium onion
225 g (8 oz) Quorn (see page
   20)
25 g (1 oz) flour
125 ml (¼ pt) vegetable stock
75 g (3 oz) tin of sweet corn
125 ml (¼ pt) soya milk or liquid
   from a tin of sweetcorn
75 g (3 oz) carrots, sliced
salt
grated nutmeg
225 g (8 oz) pastry (recipe nos.
   186, 187 or 188)

131

Quarrot pie

Set the oven at 200°C, 400°F or Gas No. 6.

Melt the margarine in a pan and fry the onion until soft.

Add the Quorn and fry for 2–3 minutes.

Add the flour and cook for 1 further minute, then remove from the heat.

Gradually stir in the stock and soya milk or liquid from the sweet corn tin.

Return to the heat and bring to the boil, stirring continuously until thick. Add the sweet corn and carrots. Season to taste with salt and nutmeg. Place in a 725 ml (1½ pt) pie dish.

Allow to cool, then cover the dish with the pastry.

Bake in the heated oven for 20–30 minutes until golden-brown.

Serve with green vegetables.

---

25 g (1 oz) margarine
1 medium onion, chopped
1 clove of garlic, crushed
   (optional)
225 g (8 oz) button mushrooms
225 g (8 oz) Quorn (see page 20)
25 g (1 oz) flour
200 ml (8 fl oz) soya milk or chicken stock (recipe no. 1)
125 ml (¼ pt) dry white wine
1 bouquet garni (see page 242)
salt

132

Crudwell casserole

Melt the margarine in a pan. Add the onion and the garlic, if used. Fry until soft but not brown.

Add the mushrooms and the Quorn and stir well. Sprinkle with the flour and cook for 1 minute.

Remove from the heat and gradually stir in the soya milk or stock. Add the wine.

Return to the heat. Bring to the boil and stir until thick. Add the bouquet garni and season with salt. Cover and simmer gently for 30 minutes to allow the flavours to develop; this can be done on top of the cooker or in the oven set at 180°C, 350°F or Gas No. 4.

Remove the bouquet garni and serve with potatoes and vegetables, or simply with plain boiled rice (recipe no. 57).

150 g (6 oz) Quorn
50 g (2 oz) crunchy peanut
butter
4 tablespoons chicken stock
(recipe no. 1) or water
2 tablespoons soy sauce
1 teaspoon grated fresh ginger
root
2 tablespoons clear honey
1 clove of garlic, crushed
1 small onion, finely chopped
2 teaspoons curry powder
1 teaspoon ground cumin
1 teaspoon ground coriander

133

Spicy satay kebab

Mix together all the ingredients except the Quorn in a shallow bowl, then stir in the Quorn chunks. Leave to stand for several hours to allow the flavour of the marinade to penetrate the Quorn.

Heat the grill to high. Remove the Quorn chunks from the marinade and thread on to skewers. Grill for 4–5 minutes until well heated through and slightly browned. Baste the kebabs with the marinade during cooking.

Serve with a vegetable stir-fry and rice (recipe nos. 85 and 57). Serve the remaining marinade separately.

Note: Pieces of chicken breast can be served in the same way.

6
Vegetable Side Dishes

List of Recipes

134

Braised red cabbage

325 g (12 oz) red cabbage
salt
125 ml ($\frac{1}{4}$ pt) white wine
50 g (2 oz) margarine
1 dessertspoon caster sugar

Set the oven at 190°C, 375°F or Gas No. 5.

Quarter, trim and then finely shred the cabbage, discarding the tough stalk. Season to taste with a little salt.

Place the cabbage in a greased casserole. Pour over the wine. Dot with the margarine and cover with a sheet of greaseproof paper. Seal tightly with a lid.

Cook in the heated oven for about 2 hours.

Just before the end of cooking, add the sugar.

135

Mange-tout

These are a variety of pea which are now becoming available almost all the year round. They are in fact much easier to grow in your garden than the more popular petits pois.

They only need to be topped and tailed before they are cooked in a little salted boiling water for about 5 minutes. Allow 75–100 g (3–4 oz) per portion.

For special occasions a little white wine added to the cooking water makes them taste even more delicious.

Drain the cooked mange-tout and brush with a little melted margarine.

Serve immediately.

136

Mushrooms with peas

225 g (8 oz) fresh peas
salt
$\frac{1}{2}$ teaspoon sugar
1 sprig of mint
2 tablespoons chicken stock
(recipe no. 1)
50 g (2 oz) margarine
8 large flat mushrooms

Bring some water to the boil; add the peas, some salt, the sugar and mint, and cook for 15 minutes until the peas are almost tender.

Drain the peas, return them to the pan and add the chicken stock and half the margarine. Cook uncovered until all the stock has been absorbed.

Wipe the mushrooms and remove the stalks (these stalks can be used in soups or sauces).

Melt the rest of the margarine in a frying pan and carefully fry the mushrooms for 5 minutes.

Place the mushroom caps on a serving dish and spoon the peas into them.

Note: This recipe can be used with frozen peas. In this case, cook the peas in boiling salted water for only 1 minute, then continue in the same way.

137

Brussels sprouts with chestnuts

150 g (6 oz) chestnuts
450 g (1 lb) small Brussels
  sprouts
500 ml (1 pt) chicken stock
  (recipe no. 1)
salt (optional)
25 g (1 oz) margarine

Set the oven at 200°C, 400°F or Gas No. 6.

First prepare the chestnuts. Make a small slit in the flat side of the nuts and place them in a baking tin. Place in the heated oven and bake for 10 minutes. During this time both the inner and outer skins will crack. Peel off the two skins while the nuts are still warm.

Wash and prepare the Brussels sprouts and make a small slit in the stem of each one.

Bring the stock to the boil and season with salt if necessary. Add the Brussels sprouts and the chestnuts; bring back to the boil, cover and simmer for 20 minutes.

Drain off the stock. Melt the margarine in a saucepan, add the Brussels sprouts and the chestnuts, and shake the pan over a moderate heat to glaze the vegetables and nuts. Serve very hot.

138

Glazed carrots

450 g (1 lb) new or old carrots
1 dessertspoon sugar
50 g (2 oz) margarine
½ teaspoon salt
1 tablespoon chopped parsley,
  to garnish

Peel or scrape the carrots and cut into rounds. Place them in a saucepan with just enough water to cover.

Add the sugar, margarine, and salt and bring to the boil.

Boil rapidly, uncovered, until the carrots are tender and all the water has evaporated.

Sprinkle with chopped parsley and serve.

139

Courgettes with mushrooms

2 tablespoons olive oil
1 clove of garlic, crushed
225 g (8 oz) courgettes, thinly
  sliced
100 g (4 oz) mushrooms, thinly
  sliced
1 teaspoon dried basil
1 teaspoon dried oregano
salt

Heat the oil in a frying pan and add the garlic. Stir-fry for 1 minute.

Add the courgettes and fry until they are soft and beginning to brown.

Add the mushrooms and the herbs. Continue cooking until the mushrooms are just beginning to soften.

Season with salt and serve with pasta.

140

Stir-fried cabbage

1 tablespoon oil
225 g (8 oz) spring cabbage,
  shredded
2 tablespoons soy sauce
100 g (4 oz) mushrooms, thinly
  sliced

Heat the oil in a large frying pan or wok and add the cabbage. Stir-fry for 2 minutes.

Add the soy sauce and cook for 1 further minute.
Finally, add the mushrooms and stir-fry for 2 further minutes.
Serve immediately.

141

Fennel

1 bulb of fennel
salt
15 g ($\frac{1}{2}$ oz) margarine, melted

Trim the fennel. Remove the leaves and stalk and wash well.

Cook in salted boiling water for 15–20 minutes until tender. *Do not overcook*.

Drain the fennel well and cut into portions. Serve with the melted margarine.

Serves 2 people.

142

Stir-fried broccoli

450 g (1 lb) broccoli
2 tablespoons olive oil
2 cloves of garlic, crushed
1 tablespoon soy sauce

Remove the heads of the broccoli and separate into florets about 2.5 cm (1 in) in length. Cut the thick green stalks diagonally across the grain into thin, slanting slices.

Heat the oil in a large frying pan or wok and when really hot add the garlic. Stir-fry for about 20 seconds, then add the broccoli florets and stalks. Continue stirring for a further 2–3 minutes only. The broccoli should be bright green, glistening with oil and still quite crisp.

Add the soy sauce and stir-fry for a further 1–2 minutes.

Serve immediately.

143

Brialmont potatoes

450 g (1 lb) even-sized potatoes
50 g (2 oz) margarine
1 onion, finely chopped
2 tablespoons chopped parsley
salt

Set the oven at 190°C, 375°F or Gas No. 5.

Scrub the potatoes and boil them in their skins for 15 minutes.

Drain and allow them to cool. Remove the skins and slice the potatoes into neat rounds about 6 mm ($\frac{1}{4}$ in) thick.

Melt the margarine in a small pan. Add the onion and cook until soft but not brown. Add the parsley and season the mixture with salt.

Oil an ovenproof dish and put the potatoes in the dish layered with the onion and parsley mixture, finishing with the onion and parsley mixture on top.

Place the dish, uncovered, in the heated oven for 20–30 minutes until the potatoes are tender and golden-brown on top.

144

German potato cakes

450 g (1 lb) even-sized potatoes
1 onion, grated
salt
a pinch of cinnamon
1 egg white
a little corn oil

Scrub the potatoes; place them in a pan and just cover with cold water. Bring the potatoes to the boil and allow to simmer for just 7 minutes. Pour off the boiling water, cover with cold water, and allow the potatoes to go cold. When cold, remove the skins and grate the potatoes.

Add the onion to the grated potatoes. Mix well, season with a little salt and the cinnamon, and add the egg white. Stir well to mix.

Heat a little oil in a frying pan and, when really hot, drop spoonfuls of the potato mixture into the pan. Flatten them with a palette knife and, when set, turn them over and cook on the other side until golden-brown.

Serve with cold fish or chicken and salad.

Makes 20 cakes.

145

Minted peas

225 g (8 oz) frozen peas
1 sprig of mint
1 small onion, chopped
1 small teaspoon sugar
salt
1 tablespoon water

Set the oven at 180°C, 350°F or Gas No. 4.

Place the peas in a greased ovenproof dish.

Add the mint, onion and sugar, and a sprinkling of salt. Pour over the water and cover the dish with a lid or kitchen foil.

Cook in the heated oven for 20 minutes.

146

Moulded cauliflower

1 medium cauliflower
salt
25 g (1 oz) margarine
1 small clove of garlic, finely
  chopped
25 g (1 oz) flaked almonds
3 tablespoons fresh
  breadcrumbs

Break the cauliflower into florets and cook in boiling salted water until tender (about 15 minutes).

Drain the cooked cauliflower carefully to remove as much water as possible.

Grease a 1 litre (2 pt) pudding basin with margarine and arrange the cauliflower florets in this. Try to keep the stalks to the centre of the basin. Cover with a plate and press gently to mould the cauliflower. Leave on one side to keep warm.

Melt the margarine in a small saucepan and fry the garlic. Add the almonds and the breadcrumbs, stir well, and cook until golden-brown.

Turn out the moulded cauliflower on to a hot serving dish and spoon over the breadcrumb mixture.

7
Salads

List of Recipes

150 g (6 oz) cooked chicken
    breast, neatly diced
½ small white cabbage, finely
    shredded
2 large carrots, grated
1 small onion, thinly sliced
4 sticks of celery, thinly sliced
salt

147

Spring salad

125 ml (¼ pt) creamy salad
    dressing (recipe no. 153)
50 g (2 oz) peanuts

Mix the diced chicken with the vegetables. Season lightly with salt.
Pour over the dressing, toss lightly, and sprinkle over the peanuts.
Serve with potatoes baked in their jackets, or with crusty bread.
Serves 2–3 people.

---

salt
225 g (8 oz) pasta shells
225 g (8 oz) tin of salmon
3 tablespoons olive oil
2 teaspoons fresh mixed herbs
    or 1 teaspoon dried mixed
    herbs

148

**Salmon pasta shell
salad**

1 lettuce
cucumber slices to garnish

Bring a saucepan of salted water to the boil and pour in the pasta
shells. Stir to prevent them sticking together, return to the boil, and
cook for 12 minutes until the pasta is just cooked, but firm.

Drain the pasta shells and rinse under cold running water until
cold. Drain and place them in a bowl.

Drain the juice from the tin of salmon into a small bowl and add the
herbs and oil. Beat the mixture with a fork.

Mix together the flaked fish and the pasta shells and arrange them
neatly on a bed of lettuce. Pour over the oil and herb mixture and
garnish the dish with cucumber slices.

Serve well chilled with wholemeal bread.

Note: Tuna fish may be used instead of salmon.

lettuce
mustard and cress
watercress
chicory
endive
green peppers, deseeded and
thinly sliced
clove of garlic

149

Green salad

A green salad can be made of one or a mixture of any green salad vegetables.

Wash the chosen salad vegetables and dry really well.

Cut a clove of garlic in two and rub the cut side around the inside of a salad bowl. Put in the salad vegetables.

Just before serving, pour in just enough herb salad dressing (recipe no. 150) to coat all the leaves of the salad. Use your hands to make sure the dressing is well mixed.

Serve immediately.

1 tablespoon olive oil
1 teaspoon corn oil
1 dessertspoon dry white wine
salt
1 teaspoon chopped fresh herbs
(e.g. parsley, thyme,
rosemary)

150

Herb dressing

Mix together the oils and add the wine. Beat with a fork until slightly thickened. Season with a pinch of salt and mix in the herbs.

Pour over the salad vegetables just before serving, and toss lightly. This is sufficient dressing for one medium lettuce.

1 clove of garlic
450 g (1 lb) peeled prawns
1 stick of celery, thinly sliced
1 green pepper, deseeded and
thinly sliced
1 lettuce
4 tablespoons creamy salad
dressing (recipe no. 153)

151

Prawn salad

Cut the garlic in half and rub the cut side around the inside of a salad bowl to give a slight garlic flavour to the salad.

Remove any black veins from the backs of the prawns, and mix the prawns with the celery and pepper.

Arrange the washed, dry lettuce in the salad bowl and pile the prawn and vegetable mixture on top.

Just before serving the salad, pour over the creamy salad dressing. Serve well chilled with fresh wholemeal bread rolls.

152

Cucumber salad

$\frac{1}{2}$ cucumber
1 teaspoon salt
1 tablespoon olive oil or good salad oil
1 teaspoon chopped mint

Peel the cucumber; split in half lengthways and then into 6 mm ($\frac{1}{4}$ in) slices. Sprinkle with the salt and allow to stand for 30 minutes, then drain off the liquid from the cucumber and add this to the oil.

Beat this mixture with a fork and add the mint.

Pour the dressing over the cucumber and serve well chilled.

153

Creamy salad dressing

1 tablespoon soya flour
3 tablespoons water
125 ml ($\frac{1}{4}$ pt) salad oil (e.g. corn, sunflower or safflower oil)
salt

Mix together the soya flour and the water to form a paste.

Place the oil in a jug and carefully pour it, drop by drop, into the paste. Whisk all the time until the dressing starts to thicken. The oil can then be added a little faster.

Add a pinch of salt and store in a covered container in the refrigerator.

Give the container a good shake before use in case the dressing has separated out.

450 g (1 lb) new potatoes
50 g (2 oz) peas (frozen or fresh)
salt
1 teaspoon chopped spring
   onion
1 teaspoon chopped parsley
a pinch of dried tarragon
creamy salad dressing (recipe
   no. 153)
lettuce leaves to serve

154

Potato salad

Wash the potatoes and boil them in their skins until tender. Plunge them into cold water and remove the skins. Cut the peeled potatoes into neat dice.

Cook the peas in a little salted water; drain and allow to cool.

Mix together the diced potatoes and cooked peas in a salad bowl, add the spring onion and the herbs, and pour over sufficient salad dressing to moisten.

Serve on a bed of lettuce.

100 g (4 oz) Patna rice
1 small onion, finely chopped
15 g ($\frac{1}{2}$ oz) margarine
100 g (4 oz) peeled prawns
50 g (2 oz) flaked almonds
2 tablespoons oil
salt

155

Rice and prawn salad

Cook the rice (recipe no. 57) and allow to go cold.

Fry the onion in the margarine until it is soft and transparent.

In a salad bowl mix together the rice, onion, prawns and almonds.

Beat the oil with a little salt and pour this over the salad. Mix well and serve well chilled.

This salad is a very good accompaniment for spiced chicken (recipe no. 97).

½ small white cabbage, finely
   shredded
2 medium carrots, grated
1 green pepper, deseeded and
   finely sliced
225 g (8 oz) cooked rice (75 g
   (3 oz) raw rice)
3 tablespoons creamy salad
   dressing (recipe no. 153)
lettuce leaves to serve
50 g (2 oz) walnuts

156

Rice and nut slaw

Mix the vegetables with the rice and add just enough creamy
dressing to moisten the mixture.

Serve on a bed of lettuce, sprinkled with the nuts.

Serve as a lunch dish on its own or leave out the nuts and serve as a
salad accompaniment to a TVP or nut cutlet dish.

1 clove of garlic, crushed
salt
3 tablespoons olive oil
100 g (4 oz) tin of tuna fish
1 red pepper
1 green pepper
lettuce leaves to serve
1 onion, thinly sliced
a small tin of anchovies
12 black olives

157

Anchovy salad

Crush the garlic with a little salt and add to the olive oil, together
with 1 tablespoon of the oil from the tin of tuna fish.

Place the red and green peppers under a hot grill and turn
frequently so that the skin becomes black and blistered. Run the
peppers under cold water to remove the skin. Cut off the stalk end,
scoop out the seeds, and shred the flesh into slices. This is best done
with a pair of kitchen scissors.

Place a bed of washed, dried lettuce on a flat serving plate.

Mix together the tuna fish, peppers and onion, and pile on top of
the lettuce.

Make a lattice of the anchovy fillets over the salad and place a black olive in each little square.

Pour over the olive oil dressing and serve well chilled.

158

Mushroom and prawn salad

225 g (8 oz) mushrooms, thinly sliced
4 tablespoons olive oil
salt
1 dessertspoon chopped fresh mixed herbs
100 g (4 oz) tinned prawns or shrimps
mustard and cress to garnish

Place the mushrooms on a flat dish.

Mix the olive oil with salt to taste and the herbs, together with 1 tablespoon of liquid from the tinned prawns or shrimps. Beat well with a fork.

Sprinkle the prawns or shrimps over the mushrooms and pour over the dressing.

Allow the salad to stand in a cool place for 1 hour before serving.

Garnish with mustard and cress and serve with brown bread and margarine.

159

Chicory salad

4 heads of chicory
25 g (1 oz) flaked almonds
oil
salt
4 large carrots, grated
125 ml (¼ pt) creamy salad dressing
(recipe no. 153)
lettuce leaves to serve

Cut the chicory into 6 mm (¼ in) slices.

Fry the almonds in a little oil until golden-brown; drain on kitchen paper and sprinkle with a little salt.

Mix together the chicory and carrot and toss in the salad dressing. Pile on to lettuce leaves and sprinkle with the almonds.

160

Carrot salad

75 g (3 oz) pine kernels
1 tablespoon walnut oil
1 dessertspoon soy sauce
225 g (8 oz) carrots, grated

Toast the pine kernels. Either place them under a hot grill and turn them over frequently, or use a dry, heavy-bottomed frying pan. If you use the pan, then heat it until hot and sprinkle in the pine kernels, shaking them all the time until they turn golden-brown.

Pour the oil into a small bowl and whisk in the soy sauce with a fork. Add the pine kernels while they are still warm.

Pour the oil and pine kernel dressing over the carrots. Stir the salad well and serve immediately.

161

Garlic and ginger salad dressing

4 tablespoons salad oil (e.g. soya, safflower, walnut, olive)
1 teaspoon garlic and ginger paste (recipe no. 112)
2 tablespoons soy sauce
salt

Place the oil in a small bowl and mix in the garlic and ginger paste.

Gradually whisk in the soy sauce and season to taste with a little salt.

This makes an excellent dressing to serve with salad ingredients such as thinly sliced mushrooms or a mixture of red/green/yellow peppers.

8
Snacks and
Savouries

List of Recipes

450 g (1 lb) potatoes
25 g (1 oz) margarine
salt
4 hard-boiled egg whites
50 g (2 oz) cooked lentils
1 teaspoon chopped chives
a little flour
1 extra egg white
browned breadcrumbs
oil for frying

162

Irish eggs

This is a good way of using up cooked mashed potatoes and lentils, or even cooked soya beans.

Mash the potatoes with the margarine and season with a little salt, if necessary. Chop the cooked egg whites and mix with the potatoes and the lentils. Add the chives. Mix really well and shape into round cakes or stick shapes.

Dip the cakes in a little flour, then in beaten egg white, and finally in browned breadcrumbs. Fry in hot oil until golden brown and drain on kitchen paper.

For quickness, these cakes can just be dipped in flour and then fried, but they do not have such a crisp coating.

Serves 2–3 people.

100 g (4 oz) dried soya beans
500 ml (1 pt) water
or
375 g (14 oz) tin soya beans
1 tablespoon oil
1 large onion, thinly sliced
2 cloves of garlic, crushed
  (optional)
25 g (1 oz) flour
1 tablespoon soy sauce

163

Soya bean hash

If using dried soya beans, soak them in the water overnight to soften. Drain and place the beans in a saucepan. Add just enough water to cover them and bring to the boil. Simmer the beans for 4 hours. Drain and reserve the liquid, adding water to make it up to 250 ml ($\frac{1}{2}$ pt).

Alternatively, if using tinned ready-cooked beans, drain off the liquid from the tin and make up to 250 ml ($\frac{1}{2}$ pt).

Heat the oil in a small pan and fry the onion and garlic, if used, until soft and transparent.

Stir in the flour and cook for 2 minutes. Remove from the heat. Add the reserved liquid from the soya beans, a little at a time, stirring continuously.

Return the mixture to the heat and cook until thickened.

Add the soya beans and soy sauce and simmer for 5 minutes.

Serve as a main meal with rice or potatoes and a green vegetable, or alternatively serve on toast as a snack with a little side salad.

Serves 2–3.

Note: Cooked soya beans will keep in the refrigerator for 4–5 days provided they are placed in a covered plastic container. It is often a good idea to cook more than you need and store until required.

It is worth noting that although using tinned beans is more convenient, buying dried beans is much cheaper.

---

15 g ($\frac{1}{2}$ oz) margarine or
1 dessertspoon oil
50 g (2 oz) flat mushrooms
salt
1 slice wholemeal bread
margarine for spreading

164

Mushrooms on toast

Heat the margarine or oil in a frying pan with a lid and add the clean and dry mushrooms. Sprinkle with a little salt and shake the pan to coat each mushroom in a little fat. Lower the heat, cover the pan, and allow the mushrooms to cook until just soft (about 5–8 minutes).

Meanwhile, toast the bread and spread lightly with margarine.

Pile the cooked mushrooms on the hot toast and serve immediately.

Serves 1 person.

Note: Field mushrooms, which are large and often open to reveal dark-brown gills, are the best ones to use because they have a fuller flavour, but cultivated mushrooms can be served instead. Field mushrooms must be peeled and washed, but cultivated ones need only to be washed.

165

Mushroom omelette

2 egg whites
a pinch of salt
1 teaspoon water
15 g (½ oz) margarine
50 g (2 oz) mushrooms, sliced
1 teaspoon oil

Break up the egg whites with a fork, add the salt and water.

Melt the margarine in a frying pan and add the mushrooms. Cook for about 2 minutes, then remove them from the pan.

Place the oil in the pan and, when it is really hot, pour in the egg mixture. Stir it with a fork until it begins to set and leave it to cook throughout.

Sprinkle the cooked mushrooms over half the omelette. Fold the other half over and serve immediately.

Serves 1 person.

166

Fried cod's roe

450 g (1 lb) fresh cod's roe,
   rinsed
1 bay leaf
1 small onion, sliced
salt
100 g (4 oz) fresh breadcrumbs
flour
1 egg white, beaten until just
   broken
oil for frying

Place the roe in a saucepan and cover with cold water. Add the bay leaf and onion, and a little salt. Bring slowly to the boil, cover the pan and simmer very gently for 15 minutes so that the roe does not break.

Take out the cooked roe and place in a small loaf tin or other container. Cover with greaseproof paper and place a weight on top and allow the roe to go cold.

When cold and pressed, cut the roe into thick slices.

Place the breadcrumbs on a flat plate, and a little flour in a dish. Dip the slices of roe, first in the flour, then in the egg white, and finally in the breadcrumbs. Press the coating on well.

Heat some oil in a frying pan and fry the slices of roe until golden-brown. Drain on kitchen paper.

Serve with toast as a substantial snack for lunch or supper.

Note: It is possible to buy cod's roe already boiled, but do make sure that it is really fresh as it dries out very quickly.

---

225 g (8 oz) dried beans (e.g. kidney, soya or chick peas) or 375 g (14 oz) tin ready-cooked beans

450 g (1 lb) potatoes, cooked and mashed

1 medium onion, finely chopped

2 teaspoons soy sauce

2 tablespoons chopped parsley

2 teaspoons ground cumin

2 teaspoons ground coriander

salt

1 egg white

a little flour

oil for frying

167

Bean burgers

If using dried beans, pour boiling water over them, then leave to soak overnight, to soften.

Drain and place the soaked beans in a saucepan. Cover with water and bring to the boil. Boil for 5 minutes, then simmer until tender. For soya beans this simmering process can take up to 4 hours. Using a pressure cooker will save you time.

If using tinned beans, drain and mash until just broken.

Mix the mashed potato into the beans, then add the onion, soy sauce, parsley and spices. Season with salt.

Add the egg white and use it to bind the mixture together. Shape the mixture into 8 round flat cakes and dip them in flour.

Fry the cakes in a little hot vegetable oil until they are golden-brown and piping hot.

Serve the burgers on their own for a snack lunch with peanut sauce (recipe no. 168) or with vegetables and an onion sauce (recipe no. 169) as a main meal.

The burgers may be made in quantity and frozen until required.

Note: Any beans may be used for this recipe. Indeed a combination of red kidney and soya bean is particularly attractive.

168

Peanut sauce

100 g (4 oz) crunchy peanut
  butter
1 tablespoon soy sauce
1 teaspoon honey
1 clove of garlic, crushed
½ teaspoon salt

Mix together all the ingredients and add just enough water to make a thick pouring sauce.
  Heat gently, stirring all the time.

169

Onion sauce

1 dessertspoon corn oil
1 medium onion, chopped
1 teaspoon flour
125 ml (¼ pt) vegetable water
1 dessertspoon soy sauce

Heat the oil in a small pan and fry the onion until soft and golden-brown.
  Stir in the flour and cook for 2 minutes.
  Remove from the heat and gradually stir in the vegetable water and soy sauce.
  Return to the heat and bring to the boil.
  Serve with nut cutlets or when a 'gravy'-type sauce is needed.

170

Arbroath smokies

1 Arbroath smokie per person
margarine

Arbroath smokies are whole small haddock which have been smoked to a light brown colour.
  Spread a little margarine over both sides of the smokies and grill for 4–5 minutes under a medium grill, until the fish are heated through.
  Serve with wholemeal bread and margarine.

150 g (6 oz) long-grain rice
150 g (6 oz) smoked haddock
2 hard-boiled egg whites,
    chopped
1 tablespoon chopped parsley
1 tablespoon chopped chives
salt
40 g (1½ oz) margarine

171

Kedgeree

Cook the rice (recipe no. 57) and fork up the grains so that they are all separate.

Heat some water in a frying pan and, when boiling, put in the smoked haddock. Cover the pan and allow to simmer for 20 minutes until the fish is cooked and will flake easily.

Drain the fish, remove all the skin and bone and flake the flesh.

Mix together the flaked haddock, rice, chopped hard-boiled egg whites and the herbs, and season with a little salt.

Melt the margarine in a saucepan and add the kedgeree. Stir carefully until really hot.

Serve with toast for supper or breakfast.

225 g (8 oz) dried pasta of your
    choice
salt
100 g (4 oz) frozen peas
2 tablespoons pesto (recipe no.
    173)

172

Pasta with pesto

Cook the pasta in salted boiling water for 10 minutes.

Add the peas, bring back to the boil and boil for a further 3 minutes.

Drain, reserving about 2 tablespoons of the cooking water.

Place the reserved water and the pesto in the pan. Heat gradually until it starts to sizzle.

Add the drained pasta and peas. Toss until well mixed.

Serve hot.

173

Pesto

2 medium cloves of garlic
100 g (4 oz) fresh basil leaves
75 g (3 oz) pine kernels
125 ml (¼ pt) virgin olive oil

Ideally, you should use a food processor or liquidizer to make pesto.

With the blade running, drop the garlic into the goblet and blend until well minced.

Add the basil leaves. When the basil is finely chopped, add the pine kernels.

With the machine still running, drizzle a fine stream of olive oil into the mixture until a thick paste is formed.

Switch off the machine and place the pesto in a small pot with a screw-lid. Use as required.

To make the pesto by hand, slice the garlic, then crush them with the flat blade of a knife. A little salt added to the garlic helps to make it into a purée.

Chop the basil leaves very finely and add to the garlic purée. Crush the pine kernels with a rolling pin until they are well broken.

Mix all the ingredients together in a small bowl and gradually add the olive oil, stirring all the time.

Note: Pesto may be stored in the refrigerator for about 1 month.

174

Scrambled egg

2 dessertspoons soya flour
2 dessertspoons soya oil
2 egg whites
2 dessertspoons soya milk
margarine
salt

In a small bowl mix together the soya flour and oil until smooth. Add the egg whites and soya milk and whisk with a fork until blended.

Melt a small knob of margarine in a small saucepan. Add the egg mixture and stir gently over a moderate heat until just set. Season to taste with salt.

Pile on to hot toast spread with a little margarine.

Note: A few sautéed mushrooms added to the scrambled egg makes an excellent breakfast or supper dish.

The mixture can also be used cold as a sandwich filling.

175

Herb bread

1 French stick
75 g (3 oz) margarine
1 teaspoon dried herbs or
    2 teaspoons chopped herbs

Set the oven of 200°C, 400°F or Gas No. 7.

Slice the loaf in the usual way, but only cut down as far as the bottom crust.

Cream the margarine and mix in the herbs.

Spread the slices of the loaf with the herby margarine. Re-form the loaf and spread a little extra margarine on top.

Wrap the loaf in some foil and bake in the heated oven for about 15 minutes.

176

Anchovy spread

1 small (50 g/2 oz) tin of
    anchovies
50 g (2 oz) margarine

Drain the oil from the anchovies and rinse the fillets in water to remove some of the saltiness. Drain and dry them on kitchen paper.

Pound the anchovies in a pestle and mortar until a smooth paste is obtained.

Cream the margarine until soft, then beat in the anchovy paste. Store in a cool place.

Serve spread on hot toast.

177

French toast

2 slices bread
yeast extract
1 egg white
salt
oil for frying

Halve the slices of bread and spread with a little yeast extract.

Beat the egg white with a pinch of salt.

Heat some oil in a frying pan. Dip the bread in the egg mixture and fry in the hot oil until golden-brown.

Drain on kitchen paper and serve hot.

Serves 1 person.

178

Salmon savouries

8 slices wholemeal bread
50 g (2 oz) margarine
100 g (4 oz) tin of salmon or
  tuna fish
salt
2 egg whites
oil for frying
cucumber slices to garnish

Remove the crusts from the bread and spread each slice with margarine.

Sandwich the slices together with the mashed salmon or tuna fish seasoned with a little salt. Cut each sandwich into four triangles.

Beat the egg whites until just broken.

Heat some oil in a frying pan.

Dip the sandwiches in the egg white and fry them in the hot oil until crisp and golden brown. Drain on kitchen paper and serve garnished with cucumber slices.

179

Spanish fluffy omelette

2 dessertspoons soya flour
4 tablespoons water
1 teaspoon vegetable oil
2 egg whites
25 g (1 oz) margarine
3 tablespoons diced vegetables
  (e.g. onion, peppers,
  mushrooms, cooked potato)

Place the soya flour in a small saucepan. Gradually pour in the water, stirring all the time until it thickens. Add the oil.

Whisk the egg whites until stiff and cut and fold into the soya mixture until well blended but still fluffy.

Heat the margarine in an omelette pan and fry the vegetables until they are soft.

Pour over the egg mixture and stir round carefully to mix. Then cook gently until the underside of the omelette is golden-brown and the mixture rises a little.

Place the pan under a hot grill to cook the top of the omelette, then serve immediately.

Serves 1 person.

180

Salted peanuts

25 g (1 oz) salt
500 ml (1 pt) water
225 g (8 oz) shelled peanuts

Add the salt to the water and soak the peanuts in this brine solution for a few minutes.

Heat a heavy-based frying pan and place a handful of the wet nuts in at a time. Shake the pan to roll the nuts around until they become dry and roasted.

Eat immediately.

You can use this recipe for other nuts, though the following method (recipe no. 181) works best for almonds.

181

Salted almonds

225 g (8 oz) whole almonds
4 tablespoons oil
salt

Skin the almonds by blanching in boiling water. Remove the skins and dry the nuts.

Heat the oil in a frying pan, slide in the nuts and fry until they are golden-brown. Do not over-cook.

Drain on kitchen paper and sprinkle on the salt while they are still hot.

182

Glucose cooler

a dash of angostura bitters
2 teaspoons liquid glucose
soda water
1 sprig of mint
ice

Shake a very little angostura bitters into a tall glass, roll it around the inside of the glass, and shake out any excess.

Add the glucose and pour in soda water. Stir to dissolve the glucose.

Crush or bruise the sprig of mint lightly between the fingers to release the flavour and add this to the drink. Add ice and serve.

Serves 1 person.

25 g (1 oz) pearl barley
scant 1 litre (2 pts) water
50 g (2 oz) granulated sugar
2 sprigs of fresh mint
soda water
a dash of angostura bitters
ice

183

Mint and barley water

Wash the barley and cover with the water. Add the sugar and mint and heat to boiling point.

Cover the pan and simmer for 40 minutes. Allow to cool.

Strain off the liquid and dilute to taste with soda water. Add a dash of angostura bitters and some ice.

9
Bread, Pastry, Cakes and Puddings

List of Recipes

1 teaspoon sugar
500 ml (1 pt) tepid water plus
   4 tablespoons
3 teaspoons dried yeast

184

675 g (1½ lb) wholemeal flour
225 g (8 oz) strong white flour

Margo's bread

1 teaspoon salt

Dissolve the sugar in the 4 tablespoons tepid water, sprinkle over the yeast, and leave in a warm place for about 5 minutes, or until the yeast has dissolved and made a frothy mixture.

In a large mixing bowl mix together the wholemeal and white flour and add the salt. Make a well in the centre of the flour and pour in the yeast mixture. Add the rest of the water. Using a wooden spoon, stir the mixture gradually, mixing in the flour until a dough is formed. Remove the dough from the bowl and knead it well until it is smooth and elastic. The kneading of the dough strengthens the gluten in the flour, and it is this which gives the loaf a good shape when baked.

When sufficiently kneaded, replace the dough in the bowl, cover with a cloth, and place in a warm place to rise. An airing cupboard is excellent for this. The dough is ready for the next stage when it has doubled in size.

Set the oven at 230°C, 450°F or Gas No. 8.

Remove the dough from the bowl and place it on a floured board. Knead the dough lightly to distribute the gas bubbles. If this is not done the bread will have large and unevenly distributed holes.

Shape the dough into loaves or rolls and place in greased tins. Leave to rise for a further 15 minutes, or until the dough has risen by a third.

Place the loaves in the heated oven. This stops further growth of the yeast. When well risen and starting to brown, after about 15 minutes, reduce the heat to 200°C, 400°F or Gas No. 6 and bake until the loaves are golden-brown and sound hollow when tapped – about 1 hour for large loaves and 30 minutes for rolls.

When cooked, remove from the tins and cool on a cooling rack.

Makes two 450 g (1 lb) loaves or 24 small bread rolls, or 3 shaped loaves, or any combination of the above.

Note: If your dried yeast does not froth within about 10 minutes it usually means that the yeast is dead. Dried yeast does not have a very long shelf life once opened.

Fresh yeast can be used instead when available. Allow 25 g (1 oz) yeast for the above mixture. Place the yeast in a small basin and add 1 teaspoon of sugar. Mix together until runny. Add 4 tablespoons tepid water and continue as above.

White bread
Make as above, only use 900 g (2 lb) plain white flour – this bread is ideal for making herb bread (recipe no. 175).

185

Oat pastry

225 g (8 oz) self-raising flour
50 g (2 oz) rolled oats
100 g (4 oz) vegetable shortening
3 tablespoons cold water

Set the oven at 200°C, 400°F or Gas No. 6.

Mix together the flour and the oats in a mixing bowl and rub in the vegetable shortening. Stir in enough water to form a dough.

Knead lightly and roll out in the usual way and use to cover pies or line flan tins.

Bake in the heated oven for 30 minutes.

Sufficient to line an 18 cm (7 in) flan ring or a 1 litre (2 pt) pie dish.

186

Short crust pastry

150 g (6 oz) white flour
½ teaspoon salt
75 g (3 oz) margarine or vegetable shortening
2 tablespoons cold water

Set the oven at 200°C, 400°F or Gas No. 6.

Sift the flour into a mixing bowl and add the salt. Add the fat and rub into the flour until the mixture resembles fine breadcrumbs.

Add the water and mix to form a dough. Lightly knead into a ball.

Roll out the pastry on a floured surface and use as required. Bake in the heated oven for 25–30 minutes.

Sufficient to line a 20 cm (8 in) flan ring or cover a 1 litre (2 pt) pie dish.

150 g (6 oz) wholemeal flour
50 g (2 oz) soya flour
salt

187

100 g (4 oz) margarine or
   vegetable shortening

Wholemeal pastry

2 tablespoons water

Set the oven at 200°C, 400°F or Gas No. 6.

Mix together the flours in a mixing bowl, add a pinch of salt, and rub in the fat until the mixture resembles fine breadcrumbs. Add enough water to form a dough.

Wrap the dough in greaseproof paper and leave in the refrigerator for 30 minutes. This allows the pastry to rest and makes it easier to roll out.

Roll out the pastry on a floured surface and use as required. Bake in the heated oven for 30 minutes.

Sufficient to line a 20 cm (8 in) flan ring or cover a 1.2–1.7 litre (2–3 pt) pie dish.

---

225 g (8 oz) self-raising flour
½ teaspoon salt

188

150 g (6 oz) block ice-cold
   vegetable fat

Rich rough puff pastry

125 ml (¼ pt) cold water

Set the oven at 200°C, 400°F or Gas No. 6.

Sift the flour into a mixing bowl and add the salt.

Dip the whole block of fat into the flour and grate on the coarse side of the grater. Keep dipping the fat into the flour as you grate, as this will keep the shreds of fat separate.

Add the water gradually, stirring with a knife until the dough binds together. Press the dough into a ball.

Roll out the pastry on a floured surface to a rectangle about 30 × 15 cm (12 × 6 in).

Fold down the top third and fold up the bottom third on top of the first fold to form a block 3 layers thick. Roll along the length until the size returns to 30 × 15 cm (12 × 6 in), then repeat the process. Place the pastry in the refrigerator to rest for 10 minutes. Repeat the procedure two more times. This will give the pastry a number of layers which will become apparent when it is cooked.

Use for pie topping and pasties. Bake in the heated oven for 20–25 minutes until golden-brown.

189

Filo pastry

450 g (1 lb) plain strong flour
1 teaspoon salt
4 tablespoons vegetable oil
about 250 ml ($\frac{1}{2}$ pt) warm water
a little extra flour
a little extra oil

Sift the flour and salt into a mixing bowl. Make a well in the centre and pour in the oil together with most of the water, and mix together to form a soft, pliable dough. Add extra water if the dough feels dry, and sprinkle in extra flour if the dough feels too sticky.

Knead the dough well for about 10 minutes until it becomes soft and springy. Cover and leave to rest for about 1 hour.

Place a tea-towel on the work surface and sprinkle with flour. (Because the pastry needs to be rolled as thinly as possible, using the tea-towel makes the handling of the finished pastry just that little bit easier.)

Brush the pastry with oil and carefully stretch to the required thickness.

190

Yeast batter

125 ml ($\frac{1}{4}$ pt) tepid water
$\frac{1}{2}$ teaspoon sugar
$\frac{1}{4}$ teaspoon dried yeast
100 g (4 oz) plain white flour
a pinch of salt
1 dessertspoon oil
1 small egg white

Place the water, which should be at about 44°C, 110°F (i.e. hand-hot) in a cup. Add the sugar and stir until dissolved. Sprinkle over the yeast and leave in a warm place for 5 minutes.

Sift the flour into a mixing bowl, add the salt, and make a well in the centre. Pour in the yeast mixture and gradually stir to mix the flour and liquid together. Beat the batter until smooth. Cover and leave in a warm place for 30 minutes, then stir in the oil.

Whisk the egg white until it is a firm snow and, when the batter is ready for use, cut and fold in the egg white with a metal spoon.

Sufficient to coat 4 good-sized fillets of fish, or about 450 g (1 lb) prawns or pieces of vegetable.

100 g (4 oz) walnuts, finely chopped
50 g (2 oz) fresh breadcrumbs
1 teaspoon cinnamon
25 g (1 oz) sugar
1 tablespoon clear honey
4 tablespoons water
1 egg white
100 g (4 oz) filo pastry (recipe no. 189)
50 g (2 oz) margarine, melted
icing sugar

191

Walnut triangles

Set the oven at 180°C, 350°F or Gas No. 5.

Mix together the walnuts, breadcrumbs and cinnamon.

Place the sugar, honey and water in a small saucepan. Boil for 1 minute.

Pour the honey mixture into the nut and crumb mixture. Add the egg white and mix well to bind the mixture.

Cut sheets of filo pastry into broad strips about 12 × 25 cm (5 × 10 in). Brush with melted margarine and fold each strip in half lengthways.

Brush again with margarine and place a teaspoonful of the nut mixture in the bottom corner and fold over to form a triangle.

Cut off the triangle and brush with margarine. Continue with the remaining mixture and pastry. Place the triangles on a greased baking sheet and bake in the heated oven for 15 minutes until golden-brown. While still hot, dust liberally with sifted icing sugar.

Makes about 36.

125 ml (¼ pt) water
50 g (2 oz) margarine
75 g (3 oz) strong plain flour
1 rounded teaspoon baking
  powder
3 egg whites
50 g (2 oz) flaked almonds

192

double quantity mock cream
  (recipe no. 207)

Almond buns

icing sugar

Set the oven at 200°C, 400°F or Gas No. 6.

Place the water and the margarine in a small saucepan. Heat until the margarine has melted, then turn up the heat until the mixture is boiling vigorously.

Very quickly, remove from the heat and add the flour and baking powder all at once. Stir well to form a ball of dough.

Beat in the egg whites a little at a time until the dough becomes smooth and glossy – an electric whisk or food processor is excellent for this.

Wet a baking sheet and place on it teaspoons of the mixture about 5 cm (2 in) apart. There should be a total of about 18 small buns. Sprinkle with the almonds.

Bake in the heated oven for 15 minutes, then increase the heat to 225°C, 425°F or Gas No. 7 and bake for a further 5–10 minutes, until golden-brown.

When the buns are cooked, pierce the side of each one to allow the steam to escape and place them on a wire rack. Leave to cool completely.

When the buns are cold, split them and fill with mock cream.

Dredge the buns well with sifted icing sugar.

Note: You could use soya cream for the filling. You could also omit the almonds and ice the filled buns with a carob icing (recipe no. 193).

193

50 g (2 oz) icing sugar
1–2 teaspoons carob powder

Carob icing

a little water

Sift the icing sugar into a bowl and mix in the carob powder. Add a few drops of water and stir to make a thin icing. This makes a very presentable mock-chocolate finish.

225 g (8 oz) carrots, grated
250 g (9 oz) wholemeal flour
350 g (13 oz) granulated sugar
$\frac{1}{2}$ teaspoon salt
1 teaspoon baking powder
1 teaspoon bicarbonate of soda
2 teaspoons cinnamon
1 teaspoon mixed spice
1 teaspoon vanilla flavour (see page 249)

194

Mavis's carrot cake

100 g (4 oz) walnuts, chopped
5 egg whites
200 ml (7 fl oz) soya oil

Set the oven at 180°C, 350°F or Gas No. 5.

Grease and line a 20 cm (8 in) cake tin.

Place the carrots in a large mixing bowl. Add all the other ingredients and mix well.

Pour the mixture into the prepared tin and bake in the heated oven for approximately 50–60 minutes or until a knife comes out clean when inserted into the centre of the cake.

Leave to cool in the tin for a few minutes, then turn the cake on to a wire rack and allow to cool completely.

When the cake is cold, split it in half and sandwich together with the filling.

Filling
50 g (2 oz) margarine
100 g (4 oz) icing sugar
vanilla flavour (see page 249)

Cream the margarine in a bowl, beat in the sifted icing sugar and flavour with a few drops of vanilla flavour.

225 g (8 oz) 80% flour
450 g (1 lb) medium oatmeal
1 teaspoon ground ginger
1 teaspoon cinnamon
1 teaspoon mixed spice
a pinch of salt
150 g (6 oz) margarine
100 g (4 oz) raw cane sugar
325 g (12 oz) black treacle
     (molasses)
½ teaspoon bicarbonate of soda
1 dessertspoon water or soya
     milk

195

Sticky parkin

Set the oven at 150°C, 300°F or Gas No. 2.

Oil and line a square baking tin 23 × 23 × 5 cm (9 × 9 × 2 in).

Mix together the flour, oatmeal, spices and salt, and rub in the margarine until the mixture resembles breadcrumbs. Add the sugar and mix well.

Warm the molasses until just liquid and pour into the centre of the mixture.

Dissolve the bicarbonate of soda in the water or milk and add to the treacle in the centre of the dry ingredients. Mix well to form a firm dough. Do not add any extra liquid.

Press the dough into the prepared tin and bake in the heated oven for 2 hours. The parkin is cooked when it feels firm to the touch and shrinks back slightly from the sides of the tin.

Turn on to a wire rack and leave to cool completely. When cold, cut into squares.

Note: This parkin improves if it is wrapped in greaseproof paper and left for 4–5 days before eating so that the spice flavours mellow and the cake becomes more sticky.

---

100 g (4 oz) margarine
75 g (3 oz) brown sugar
50 g (2 oz) crunchy peanut
     butter
150 g (6 oz) wholemeal flour

196

Peanut crunchies

Set the oven at 180°C, 350°F or Gas No. 4.

Cream the margarine and sugar together until light and fluffy.

Beat in the peanut butter and stir in the flour.

Knead to make a firm dough, roll out to 6 mm (¼ in) thick, and cut into fingers.

Bake in the heated oven on a greased baking sheet for 15–20 minutes. Allow to cool before removing from the baking sheet.

Makes 36.

197

Muesli

1 tablespoon mixed nuts
2 tablespoons rolled oats
1 dessertspoon soya flour
a pinch of mixed spice or
   cinnamon
1 dessertspoon brown sugar

Chop the nuts roughly and place in a bowl with the rolled oats.

Sprinkle over the soya flour, spice and sugar, and mix well.

Add enough water to make a thick mixture.

Serve immediately.

Serves 2 people.

198

Portadown cake

150 g (6 oz) margarine
150 g (6 oz) raw cane sugar
1 dessertspoon instant coffee
1 tablespoon hot water
1 teaspoon baking powder
150 g (6 oz) wholemeal flour
3 egg whites
honey or Portadown cream
   (recipe no. 199)
icing sugar

Set the oven at 190°C, 375°F, Gas No. 5.

Grease two 20 cm (7 in) sandwich tins and flour lightly, shaking off any excess.

Cream together the margarine and sugar until light and fluffy. Dissolve the coffee in the water and beat into the mixture.

Mix the baking powder with the flour.

Whisk the egg whites until stiff.

Add both the egg whites and the flour to the creamed mixture and then, using a metal spoon, carefully cut and fold in until the mixture is a uniform colour and texture. Try not to over-mix as this will destroy the volume and the lightness of the egg whites.

Divide the mixture between the prepared tins and bake in the centre of the heated oven for 25–30 minutes. The cakes are cooked if the mixture springs back when gently pressed with a finger.

Turn the cakes on to a wire rack and leave to cool completely.

When the cakes are cold, sandwich them together with honey or Portadown cream, and dust the top with sifted icing sugar.

199

Portadown cream

2 dessertspoons dandelion coffee or 1 dessertspoon instant coffee
2 dessertspoons cornflour
125 ml ($\frac{1}{4}$ pt) soya milk
50 g (2 oz) margarine
1 dessertspoon clear honey

In a small bowl mix together the coffee and the cornflour and blend with a little of the soya milk to make a thin cream.

Put the rest of the soya milk on to boil and, when boiling, pour this on to the cornflour mixture. Return to the saucepan and bring back to the boil, stirring all the time. Allow the mixture to go cold.

Cream together the margarine and honey and then beat in the cold cornflour mixture until smooth. Use to sandwich the Portadown cake (recipe no. 198), or whenever a cream filling is required.

200

Safa cake

150 g (6 oz) soft margarine
150 g (6 oz) caster sugar
4 egg whites
225 g (8 oz) semolina
2 teaspoons baking powder
100 g (4 oz) ground almonds
1 tablespoon water

Set the oven at 180°C, 350°F or Gas No. 4.

Grease and line a 23 cm (9 in) cake tin.

Cream together the margarine and sugar until light and fluffy.

Beat in 2 of the egg whites, one at a time, beating well to make the mixture as light as possible.

Whisk the 2 remaining egg whites to a foam.

Mix together the semolina, baking powder, and ground almonds.

Using a metal spoon, cut and fold the dry ingredients into the creamed mixture, then stir in the whisked egg whites. Add a little water to get a dropping consistency.

Place the mixture in the prepared tin and bake in the heated oven for 40 minutes until firm and brown.

Allow to cool slightly before removing from the tin.

Place the cake on a wire rack and leave to cool completely.

201

Coffee and walnut cakes

2 egg whites
100 g (4 oz) raw cane sugar
1 tablespoon instant coffee
25 g (1 oz) walnuts, chopped

Set the oven at 150°C, 300°F or Gas No. 2.

Line a baking sheet with non-stick silicone paper or greased greaseproof paper.

Place the egg whites in a bowl and add the sugar. Place the bowl over a pan of boiling water and whisk together until the mixture is really thick and heavy. This mixture is best made with a hand-held electric whisk as it does take 10–15 minutes to get the mixture really thick.

Remove the bowl from the heat and stir in the coffee and the walnuts.

Place spoonfuls of the mixture on the prepared baking sheet and bake in the heated oven for 25 minutes.

Allow the cakes to cool completely, then remove from the baking sheet.

Makes 18.

202

Macaroons

2 egg whites
150 g (6 oz) vanilla sugar
100 g (4 oz) ground almonds
25 g (1 oz) ground rice
flaked almonds to decorate

Set the oven at 150°C, 300°F or Gas No. 2.

Line a baking sheet with non-stick silicone paper or rice paper.

Reserve 1 teaspoon of the egg white to use as a glaze later and put the rest of the egg whites into a large bowl.

Whisk the egg whites until they are stiff and then whisk in the sugar 1 tablespoon at a time. Then, with a metal spoon, cut and fold in the ground almonds and the ground rice.

Place the mixture in 20 small heaps on the prepared baking sheet, flatten them out slightly, and place a flaked almond on the top of each one.

Brush the macaroons over with the reserved egg white and bake in the heated oven for 40 minutes until pale golden. Allow them to cool, then remove them from the paper or tear round the rice paper. When the macaroons are cold, store in an airtight tin.

203

Honey and sesame seed wafers

225 g (8 oz) clear honey
225 g (8 oz) sesame seeds
vegetable oil

Place the honey in a heavy saucepan. Heat gently and bring to the boil.

Add the sesame seeds and cook gently until large bubbles appear on the surface.

To test for setting, drop a little of the mixture into a bowl of cold water. If the drop can be rolled into a soft ball then the mixture is ready.

Pour the mixture on to a well-oiled tray and spread out about 6 mm ($\frac{1}{4}$ in) thick. Leave until cold, then cut into wafers and store in an airtight container.

These are delicious for those who yearn for something really sweet and crunchy. The sesame seeds taste like roasted almonds.

1 tablespoon soya flour
2 tablespoons water
1 dessertspoon oil
250 ml ($\frac{1}{2}$ pt) soya milk
2 egg whites, beaten
25 g (1 oz) sugar
4 slices bread
margarine for spreading
honey for spreading
50 g (2 oz) almonds, shredded
cinnamon

204

Pantec pudding

Set the oven at 160°C, 325°F or Gas No. 3.

Mix the soya flour and the water together to form a smooth paste. Heat until boiling in a saucepan and cook until thick. Remove from the heat and whisk in the oil until the mixture resembles pale egg yolk.

To this mixture add the soya milk and the egg whites. Return to the heat and bring to the boil, stirring all the time. Remove from the heat and stir in the sugar.

Remove the crusts from the bread and spread the slices with margarine and honey. Cut each slice into quarters and arrange in a greased pie dish. Sprinkle over the almonds and pour over the soya 'custard'. Sprinkle with cinnamon to taste and bake in the heated oven for 30 minutes until set. Serve hot.

---

150 g (6 oz) wholemeal flour
a pinch of salt
100 g (4 oz) vegetable
   shortening
1 tablespoon water

For the filling
125 g (5 oz) golden syrup
100 g (4 oz) wholemeal
   breadcrumbs

205

Treacle tart

Set the oven at 200°C, 400°F or Gas No. 6.

Place the flour and salt in a mixing bowl and rub in the fat until the mixture resembles fine breadcrumbs.

Stir in the water to make a dough. Because this is such a short pastry, it is best to leave it on one side or in the refrigerator for 30 minutes before rolling out.

Roll out the pastry and use to line a 20 cm (8 in) shallow pie plate. Prick the bottom of the pastry well.

To make the filling, warm the golden syrup, stir in the breadcrumbs, and pour the mixture into the lined pie plate.

Roll out the pastry trimmings into strips 6 mm ($\frac{1}{4}$ in) wide and make a lattice over the syrup.

Bake the tart in the heated oven for 25–30 minutes. Serve hot or cold.

206

Hazelnut meringue cake

100 g (4 oz) hazelnuts
4 egg whites
225 g (8 oz) caster sugar
2 teaspoons cornflour
a pinch of cream of tartar
icing sugar

Set the oven at 190°C, 375°F or Gas No. 5.

Grease and flour the sides of two 20 cm (8 in) sandwich tins and line the bottoms with a round of non-stick baking paper.

Place the hazelnuts in the heated oven for 8–10 minutes to brown the nuts. Allow the nuts to cool slightly and rub off the papery skins. Place the nuts in a grinder or liquidizer and grind them.

Whisk the egg whites until really stiff and dry, then whisk in the sugar, 1 tablespoonful at a time. When all the sugar has been added the meringue should feel thick and heavy.

Whisk in the cornflour and the cream of tartar.

Using a metal spoon, stir in the prepared nuts as lightly as possible.

Divide the mixture between the prepared tins, level the top, and bake in the heated oven for 30–40 minutes until the top is crisp and brown and the inside soft. Allow to cool and turn out on to cooling trays. Allow to go cold before assembling the cake.

Sandwich the two halves of the hazelnut meringue together with the mock cream (recipe no. 207) and dust the top liberally with sifted icing sugar.

Serves 4–6 people.

207

Mock cream

15 g (½ oz) cornflour
125 ml (¼ pt) soya milk
25 g (1 oz) margarine
25 g (1 oz) vanilla sugar

Blend the cornflour with a little of the soya milk, and put the rest on to boil.

Pour the boiling soya milk on to the cornflour, stirring all the time. Return the mixture to the pan and cook for 2 minutes until very thick. Allow this mixture to go cold.

Cream together the margarine and vanilla sugar until light and fluffy.

Gradually beat in the cold cornflour mixture, a little at a time, until the mixture is again light and fluffy.

208

Alexandra biscuits

100 g (4 oz) margarine
100 g (4 oz) raw cane sugar
1 egg white
225 g (8 oz) wholemeal flour

Cream the margarine and sugar until very light-textured. Add the egg white and beat well. Stir in the flour and mix to a dough.

Divide the mixture in half and roll each piece into a sausage shape 7.5 cm (3 in) long. Wrap the dough shapes in greaseproof paper and place in the refrigerator for between 30 minutes and 1 hour for the dough to become firm.

Set the oven at 190°C, 375°F or Gas No. 5.

Slice the rolls into 6 mm (¼ in) slices and place them on a greased baking sheet. Prick the biscuits and bake in the heated oven for 15 minutes. Store in an airtight tin when cold.

Makes 24.

209

Honey pancakes

100 g (4 oz) flour
a pinch of salt
2 egg whites
125 ml (¼ pt) soya milk
1 tablespoon oil

To serve
clear honey
2 tablespoons sugar
1 teaspoon cinnamon

Place the flour and salt in a mixing bowl. Make a well in the centre and add the egg whites and a little of the soya milk.

Using a wooden spoon, stir the mixture, bringing in flour from the sides to form a smooth batter. Beat well for 5 minutes, using an electric mixer if preferred.

Stir in the rest of the soya milk and allow the batter to stand for 1 hour, so that the starch grains soften and the mixture thickens a little. When ready to use, the batter should be the consistency of a thick cream which pours easily.

Place the oil in a small frying pan and heat until very hot. Pour this oil into the batter mixture and stir well. This makes the batter slightly oily so that there is no need to grease the frying pan after each pancake.

Pour the batter into the pan and roll it around to give a thin layer on the bottom. As the batter goes in it should sizzle and start to cook immediately. If the pan is not hot enough the pancake may stick.

When the pancake is set, turn it over and cook on the other side.

Store the pancakes piled up on a hot plate until needed.

To serve, spread the pancakes with honey and roll them up. Sprinkle them with a mixture of sugar and cinnamon and serve hot. Maple syrup can be used as an alternative to honey.

Makes 6–8 pancakes.

210

Carob bavarois

2 dessertspoons carob powder
125 ml ($\frac{1}{4}$ pt) soya milk
2 dessertspoons soya flour
1 dessertspoon corn oil
2 tablespoons icing sugar
7 g ($\frac{1}{4}$ oz) powdered gelatine
2 dessertspoons water
100 g (4 oz) margarine
2 egg whites

Mix the carob powder with a little of the soya milk to form a thin paste, and heat the rest of the milk in a saucepan. Add the carob mixture and heat through.

Mix together the soya flour and the oil, add this to the soya milk, and bring to the boil, stirring all the time. Cook for 2 minutes, then stir in the icing sugar.

Place the gelatine and water in a small cup and place the cup in a bain-marie. Heat until the gelatine is dissolved and crystal-clear.

Add the dissolved gelatine to the carob mixture, and remove from the heat.

Add the margarine, a little at a time, and stir until it has all been absorbed.

Whisk the egg whites until stiff and cut and fold them into the carob mixture, so that they are evenly distributed throughout the mixture.

Pour into small individual dishes and allow to set.

This very rich sweet will serve 4–6 people.

2 dessertspoons soya flour
4 tablespoons water
1 teaspoon oil

211

2 egg whites
extra oil for frying

Fluffy omelette

maple or golden syrup to serve

Place the soya flour in a small saucepan. Gradually add the water, stirring continuously, until the mixture is smooth. Cook until thick, then add the oil.

Whisk the egg whites until stiff. Add the soya mixture, using a fork to mix until well blended but still fluffy.

Heat oil in a frying pan until really hot. Pour in the egg and soya mixture. Cook gently until the underside of the omelette is golden-brown and the mixture rises a little.

Place the pan under a hot grill to cook the top of the omelette.

Serve immediately with maple or golden syrup.

Serves 2 people.

4 slices bread
honey for spreading
2 egg whites

212

oil for frying
1 tablespoon sugar

Honey dreams

1 teaspoon cinnamon

Sandwich the slices of bread together with the honey and press together firmly. Cut each sandwich into 4 triangles and remove the crusts, if desired.

Place the egg whites in a shallow dish and beat until well broken. Dip the sandwiches in the beaten egg white and immediately fry them in very hot oil until golden-brown. Drain on kitchen paper.

Mix together the sugar and cinnamon and sprinkle this over the honey dreams.

Serve hot.

Serves 2 people.

213

Carob custard

25 g (1 oz) cornflour
2 dessertspoons carob powder
25 g (1 oz) sugar
500 ml (1 pt) soya milk

Mix together the cornflour, carob powder and sugar in a small bowl. Add a little of the soya milk to make a thin cream.

Place the rest of the milk in a saucepan and bring to the boil. Pour a little of the boiling milk on to the carob mixture, stirring all the time, and then pour this back into the milk in the saucepan.

Return the pan to the heat, stirring all the time, until the custard thickens. Cook for 1 minute.

Serving suggestions
Add 50 g (2 oz) chopped mixed nuts to the custard and serve in individual bowls.

Increase the cornflour to 50 g (2 oz) and pour the custard into a mould. Chill until set, unmould, and serve with canned soya cream.

214

Carob spread

100 g (4 oz) margarine
2 tablespoons golden syrup
2 dessertspoons carob powder
50 g (2 oz) flaked almonds

Cream together the margarine and golden syrup until well mixed.
Beat in the carob powder, then stir in the flaked almonds.
Store in a jam jar and spread on bread or toast.

215

Peanut brittle

225 g (8 oz) granulated sugar
225 g (8 oz) chopped peanuts

Place the sugar in a heavy-based saucepan and place over a high heat. As soon as the sugar starts to melt, reduce the heat, and shake the pan so that the sugar melts evenly and turns a light brown. Do not stir the sugar and take care not to overcook. It is ready when a small amount dropped into cold water forms a crisp ball.

Line a tin with greased greaseproof paper and sprinkle over the coarsely chopped peanuts in a single layer. When the sugar is ready, pour it over the peanuts.

Allow the brittle to go hard, then break into pieces.

Store in an airtight tin.

216

Coffee walnuts

Makes 40
100 g (4 oz) ground walnuts
225 g (8 oz) icing sugar
4 tablespoons strong coffee
2–3 drops vanilla flavour (see page 249)
1 teaspoon rosewater
1 tablespoon granulated sugar

Mix the walnuts with the icing sugar.

Gradually add the coffee and vanilla flavour to form a stiff mixture.

Moisten your hands with rosewater and form the nut mixture into small balls about the size of a walnut.

Roll them in the granulated sugar and leave to harden.

Note: The coffee walnuts will keep in an airtight tin for 2–3 weeks and are good to serve with coffee after dinner.

217

Flapjacks

100 g (4 oz) margarine
65 g (2½ oz) sugar
1 tablespoon golden syrup
125 g (5 oz) rolled oats
a little extra margarine

Set the oven at 180°C, 350°F or Gas No. 4.

Melt the margarine, sugar and syrup in a saucepan.

Stir in the oats and mix well.

Grease a 19 × 32 cm (7 × 13 in) Swiss roll tin with margarine.

Spread the mixture out in the prepared tin to within 1 cm (½ in) of the edge.

Bake in the heated oven for 15–20 minutes until golden-brown.

Allow to cool in the tin, then before completely cold cut into finger slices.

Makes 18–24 flapjacks.

Appendices

Questions and
Answers

Over the past seventeen years, Mary has met and talked to hundreds of people suffering from either osteo- or rheumatoid arthritis, and the same questions come up time and time again.

We have put all these questions and their answers together, and we hope that here you will be able to find the answers to some of the things that have been worrying you.

Am I correct in assuming that Dr Dong's diet is based on food allergies?
Yes. The whole principle of Dr Dong's diet is that we suffer an allergic reaction to some of the things we eat.

How long will it take before the diet works?
This is a question that everyone asks. In my case it took two weeks; in your case it could be longer. But you should have a good idea in three to five weeks. When the diet is working, in most cases the sign will be a foul taste in the mouth. This is caused by the elimination of toxins from the system. This also happens to people who fast. The foul taste and mouth odour will clear as you get better and only reappear when you make the odd diversion. If the diet is not working, then the cause may be coffee or margarine or honey or even nuts.

Should you stick strictly to the diet to gain full relief?
Yes, 100%. In time, when you are feeling better, you can add foods to find out if you get a reaction from them.

Will this diet cure arthritis?
No, not to my knowledge. My blood tests are positive even today. The diet should bring relief from stiffness and pain.

How do you, Mary, stand the diet?
How do you, Reader, stand the pain?

Can I relax from the diet occasionally?
That is up to you. I sometimes do at parties, but not very much. I keep away from tomatoes, soup, alcoholic drinks (except beer and the occasional glass of wine). Diversions from the diet in the early stages can mean seventy-two painful hours. Make sure that you think it is worth it.

Is it worth giving up my favourite foods to try the diet?
That is up to you. You have the pain, you have the stiffness, therefore you must decide.

Can the diet do me any harm?
No, so long as you keep it well balanced. Help on this subject can be found in the chapter dealing with basic nutrition.

Do I need to take extra vitamin tablets?
There should be no need to take added vitamins if the balanced diet outlined in the chapter on nutrition is followed reasonably closely. Only a few vitamins, notably B$_{12}$, nicotinic acid and folic acid, can be stored in the body. An excess of any of the others is immediately filtered from the blood stream by the kidneys. Thus, excess amounts taken in the form of pills would almost be completely wasted. There are occasions, particularly during pregnancy and lactation, or a specific illness, when extra nutrients could be prescribed by a doctor, and these would then be necessary. But, generally, a good balanced diet is by far the best way of obtaining all the essential nutrients the body needs to carry out its functions correctly.

Does my food have to be complicated?
First you must decide what sort of cook you are. Would you describe yourself as a *coq-au-vin* type cook, or do you think that chicken and chips is more your style? Maybe you fall somewhere between these two types.

Few people are prepared to go to great trouble to prepare each meal as though it were a feast, apart from the fact that many people are far too busy anyway. Get the idea from the very start that you can continue your style of cooking as before; all you will do is change some of the foods you cook.

Firstly, you will have to reorganize your thoughts on *what* you can eat rather than how you will cook it. Having sorted that out, you will just go about your cooking exactly as before, and use substitutes when necessary.

Snacks are a bit of a problem to start off with. Things like cheese on toast or a quick tin of baked beans will, of course, be out. So you must find some quick and easy snacks which you like. There are some ideas in the recipe section. It is important that your store cupboard always contains the ingredients to make your favourite snacks, so that you will not be tempted to go off the diet for the sake of a little time.

Does the diet have to cost a lot of money?
No. There is no need for you to spend any more money on food now than you did before. You are cutting out three groups of food which

you have been buying every week, i.e. dairy produce, fruit and meat. The savings on these can be used to buy fish and some interesting vegetables.

You will also find that, as you cannot buy commercially prepared foods, the savings on these alone will be considerable. Initially, the thing it will cost is time. A little more time to think about what you are going to eat, and a little more time in preparation.

Are all health foods all right?
Not within the scope of the diet. Some products contain chemicals like monosodium glutamate or hydrolysed vegetable protein. Care should be taken to read the labels, especially when choosing textured vegetable protein or ready-made nut mixtures.

Can one eat yeast spread?
Yes, so long as it is yeast extract and not beef, and free from chemicals.

Can I have bananas?
No, they are a fruit. You can introduce them into your diet after a year or so and see if you get a reaction – you most probably will.

Is cottage cheese acceptable?
No, it is not. It is made from milk and milk is not on the diet.

Can I drink decaffeinated coffee?
Yes, decaffeinated coffee is perfectly acceptable.

Can I take sweeteners in my tea or coffee?
No. Sweeteners are full of chemicals. Try drinking your tea or coffee weaker than usual, without milk or sugar, and see if you can acquire the taste.

Can I drink grapefruit juice?
No: very painful. Try carrot juice instead.

I have eaten fruit all my life. How can I replace all the goodness if I give it up?
Fruit is most missed from the diet because it is a refreshing and delicious addition. The fact that it is omitted does not cause a dietary deficiency, as long as vegetables are eaten. Fruit contains some energy-giving sugar and a small amount of protein. Vitamins A and

C are contained in varying amounts dependent on the variety of the fruit and its age. It also contains potassium, magnesium, iron and calcium in small amounts. All of these can be obtained from vegetable and other sources in the diet.

Can I have a glass of wine?

Not recommended. Wine as it is drunk by the glass is too acidic for most arthritics to handle. A little used in cooking is acceptable because the wine is broken down and changed during the cooking process. However on a special occasion if you wish to drink a glass then choose from wines such as Sauternes – they are produced by a special natural process and tend to be rich yet sweet. However bear in mind that even these may cause a reaction.

What can I drink to be sociable?

This is a very good question. I tend to drink water with some ice in it. It looks just like a gin and tonic. Who is to know? Most people will admire you for being on the diet anyway. One does not have to drink to be sociable.

Is a vegetarian cheese acceptable on the diet?

No. Vegetarian cheese is cheese without rennet, not without milk.

The diet stipulates that I cannot drink milk. Where do I obtain my daily supply of calcium?

The main sources of calcium in this diet are smelt, sprats and tinned fish, because the bones are eaten, and watercress, parsley, soya flour and dark green vegetables. The body quickly adapts to taking calcium from these and other foods when it is denied milk. If you substitute soya milk for cow's milk, then the soya milk supplies the calcium required.

May I use white flour?

White flour is obtained from milling wheat. The bran and the wheat germ are removed and all that is left is the white endosperm which gives the white flour. To put back some of the goodness removed by taking out the bran and wheat germ, powdered chalk, an iron compound, nicotinic acid and vitamin B are added. As long as it stops there, this white flour is perfectly acceptable within the diet, and is indeed very useful for making the lighter sorts of cakes, pancakes and puddings.

Unfortunately, most of the household flour sold in the shops contains bleaching and improving agents which are best avoided. If you want to buy a white flour, buy an 80% extraction flour from a health food shop. Wholemeal flour is protected by law from all additives.

Is brown sugar better than white sugar?

All commercially produced sugars are virtually the same. They are processed from beet and cane and occasionally maple, but the chemical composition is the same. The more the refinement, the whiter and finer the sugar, and more of it is needed to obtain the same degree of sweetness. Brown sugar retains some of the colour and flavour of the raw cane sugar, but it is in no way a better source of nutrient than ordinary white sugar.

Molasses remains when the sugar has been crystallized out of the beet or cane sugar solutions, and this is used to make treacle and golden syrup.

All sugars are usually acceptable on the diet, but they can be left out of any diet completely without any harm. Sugar only provides energy and this can be obtained from the natural sugar in vegetables; so most sugar we eat is superfluous and only feeds our sweet tooth.

Is there a substitute for chocolate?

There is a powder on the market, made from the pod of the carob tree, which tastes remarkably like chocolate and can be used in a variety of recipes to produce chocolate-type puddings and sauces.

There are also on the market 'diet' bars of chocolate, sometimes made from carob powder. But do look at the labels carefully. Sometimes the bars are made from carob and milk and others from chocolate and soya milk, neither of which is acceptable.

What am I missing when I do not eat egg yolks?

Mainly animal fat, but there is no other nutrient which cannot be obtained from a balanced, varied diet.

Is there an alternative to rice?

Rice is useful in this diet because it can form the basis for interesting and varied vegetable dishes. Rice is essentially a filler; it adds bulk to the diet and makes one feel satisfied. Bread and potatoes do the same sort of thing, but they are not empty foods as they all contain other nutrients beside carbohydrate. If rice is not liked, the chances are that only the white polished rice has been tried, so it is worth buying the brown rice obtainable from health food shops and trying that. It certainly has more taste than the white polished rice, a much firmer texture and, of course, contains more nutrients, particularly from the vitamin B complex.

Help! I can't cook.
This is a bit of a problem because buying processed food is out. But you do not have to be a superb cook to feed yourself good and nourishing fare. Learn how to cook rice, first of all. Then you have a basis for many tasty dishes. By adding lightly fried vegetables and canned fish to your rice you have a meal to impress anyone.

If I have gout, will the diet help?
Gout is a form of arthritis, therefore it should be helped by following the diet. But experience has shown that peas, beans and too much wholemeal bread do cause pain in the feet.

I do not want to lose weight. How can I prevent this happening?
Because this diet cuts out animal food, this also cuts out a lot of fat which is not usually noticed, so a drop in weight initially is quite usual. Now, although this is usually quite beneficial to most arthritics, there are some people who need to maintain their body weight from the start. In this case it is best to use more oil in your cooking than usual and include extra carbohydrate in the form of bread and other cereals.

What quantities of fish and vegetables do I need for general good health?
In the chapter on nutrition you will find the recommended amounts of all the essential nutrients needed to maintain good health. On average, though, a portion of fish would mean 100–150 g (4–6 oz). A portion of potatoes means 125–150 g (5–6 oz) and of green vegetables 75–100 g (3–4 oz). Obviously these are minimum requirements which are not difficult to obtain with a fair-sized appetite. Beyond this minimum requirement, cereals should be eaten so that the body feels satisfied, but never bloated.

Why are tomatoes excluded from the diet?
Tomatoes are a fruit; they grow from flowers and produce seeds. It has been found from experience that tomatoes do give quite a lot of pain to the arthritic, so they should be avoided. Along with tomatoes, marrows and cucumbers are also fruits, but some people find that they can tolerate these. Do keep this in mind when you choose to eat marrows, courgettes or cucumbers; they may cause pain. Keep off

them initially and introduce them to your diet as you begin to feel better, then you will be able to tell how they affect you.

I have a sweet tooth. What can I do about it?
Well, I suppose the answer is nothing, except learn to eat only those sweet things which come within the diet. Sugar is allowed in the diet, but it has been pointed out that sugar is not essential to a balanced diet; so if you can cure your desire for sweet things you will be a lot healthier. However, I do know the feeling after a nice meal when you know that something sweet would just end things off nicely. Well, sadly, all the manufactured candies and chocolates are out; they rely on chemicals more often than not and, even if you find carob chocolate, you will probably find that it is made with milk.

There are a few sweet recipes in Part II which I hope will fit the bill and there are also some ideas for puddings and sweet spreads to go on your teatime bread.

Can smoking cause pain?
Yes. Some arthritics find that hands and wrists are particularly affected by smoking.

Can the diet help arthritic animals?
Yes. Many animals, especially dogs, are prone to arthritis, and they can benefit from the principles of the diet in the same way as humans.

I have been on the diet for some time now and seem to be in more pain.
This has been known to happen to some people, not many. First look at the past few days and make sure that you have not put too much overwork or stress on your body, as this may be one cause. Another cause, as with headaches which sometimes ensue, could be the body reacting to the process of eliminating toxins, diversions from your diet can also cause pain especially in the early stages. Lastly it could be the medication you are taking.

Rest and warmth, plus going straight back on the diet are highly recommended. For rest and warmth, try taking a hot bath; if you have high blood pressure or a weak heart avoid hot baths, have a warm one instead with something in like epsom salts, then wrap up warm and relax either by going to bed, resting in your favourite armchair or on the sofa. If possible, try to sleep as you will probably feel tired.

If pain is due to dietary diversions, go straight back on to the diet. You may find that you have also got a foul taste in the mouth. If you have this is a good sign as it also shows that the system is clearing itself of the toxins. Pain should be greatly reduced or disappear completely as the foul taste gets better.

If in doubt, consult your doctor, especially if you think it is due to medication. DO NOT cut out medication without medical advice first.

My doctor says I must learn to live with arthritis.
Being on this diet you are doing just that. You are learning to live within its limitations. As you progress through the diet, I hope that these limitations will become less.

Food Additives

It would be impracticable to ban all food additives, as without them the food industry would have great problems in supplying the needs of the urban population of the world. However, there is no need for the average person to buy quite as many manufactured foods, because an exclusive diet of shop-bought, rather than home-made, dishes builds up an enormous level of added chemicals, which our bodies do not need.

For the rheumatoid or osteoarthritic, these food additives can mean pain, so they must be avoided, and the only way this can be done is to read carefully every label on every jar, tin or packet you pick up whilst shopping. You will probably find it quite frightening.

Of course, not everything is labelled. Vegetables, for instance, do not come with a little list attached of all the things that were put on the ground in which they were grown. So, if practical, grow your own vegetables or buy organically grown ones.

Frozen chickens lack labels telling you what the chicken ate, but they will tell you if the chicken has been injected with any chemical; so try to buy fresh free-range chickens whenever possible.

Obviously, to do this is not always possible, particularly for reasons of cost. Organically grown vegetables are usually very expensive, and fresh chickens cost more than frozen ones, but do explore the sources of food available and buy as little mass-produced food as possible. To give you some idea of what goes into our food, listed below you will find the most common groups of additives, and the reasons why they are used.

Preservatives

In the modern world in which we live, there is no doubt that, without preservatives, foodstuffs would perish and could not be transported to the United Kingdom and distributed without serious dangers to the nation's health.

The only pure preservative is freezing, and unless this is carefully controlled during the transport and storage of goods, problems can arise and food poisoning can result.

In the main, preservatives are used in the meat and fruit canning industry, neither of which product concerns the arthritic who is using Dr Dong's diet. However, preservatives used in foods which are on the diet must be carefully looked at.

Sulphur dioxide

This is used as a preservative in many foods, including wines, beers and other soft drinks. The other place where sulphur dioxide may be found is in dried vegetables. Potatoes and other vegetables can be accelerated freeze dried (AFD) and the sulphur dioxide is added as a further preservative. So it is always wise to look at these packets.

Antioxidants

This is a big group of additives, very widely used in food processing.

Antioxidants are used with oils and fats to prevent slow oxidation, which produces rancid flavours and makes the fats inedible. Without the use of antioxidants, the fats would be rancid before they could be transported and delivered to the shops.

There are fourteen permitted antioxidants used in the food industry; six of them are subject to specific control, but the others are not so controlled because they are naturally occurring. The main ones found in edible oils and fats, including soft margarine, are: butylated hydroxyanisole (BHA), butylated hydroxytoluene (BHT) or any mixture of BHA and BHT. All these are best avoided.

Emulsifiers and stabilizers

These are used extensively in the food processing industry. The emulsifiers help to produce foods which look attractive to begin with, and the stabilizers ensure that they maintain their looks and texture during transport and storage.

Natural emulsions occur when a creamy salad dressing is made by whisking oil and water together at great speed and using soya flour as the emulsifier. When whisked the ingredients hold together like a mayonnaise. But this common household emulsion will separate out if left for any length of time and, although not a problem for short-term use in a small household, it is not acceptable in a shop-bought product. Because of this, the industry uses stabilizers as well as emulsifiers, so the product stays the same throughout its shelf life.

There are many emulsifiers; they differ chemically and this determines which combination of foods they will emulsify. There are fifty-seven specific substances, including edible gum, lecithin, agar and alginates. Most of them are used in food processing and should be avoided, but lecithin, the one present in soft margarines, may be tolerated, although it is best to treat this with a certain amount of caution.

Colourings

If one asks if colouring is essential in the food processing industry, in the same way that antioxidants are necessary, then the answer must be an emphatic 'No'. The only justification for their use is aesthetic. We get what we want, and it would appear that the majority of people like foods which look the right colour. An example of this is tinned peas. When peas are tinned and heat-treated they lose their chlorophyll and the resulting peas are a greyish-green instead of the yellowish-green we expect. So the food industry puts back the colour artificially. Close your eyes and they would all taste the same.

Colourings are used in the canning industry, as well as in many processed foods, and they will appear on the label as permitted colourings, which can be either natural or synthetic. In any case, they should be avoided. It is best to choose fresh or frozen vegetables whenever possible.

Flavours and solvents

These two groups of additives have come to the fore in recent years, mainly because the housewife today spends about half the time in the kitchen that she used to spend twenty years ago. She now relies heavily on the food processing industry, to provide tasty foods which need little or no preparation. Not only that, she wants to be able to go to the shop next week and get the same meal, tasting the same. To produce such food the industry uses flavouring agents and, because uniformity is important, chemically produced flavours are used. These flavours are available all the year round at the same strength, and this of course is impossible with the natural product.

The EC has listed over 2000 permitted flavouring substances, and these are used extensively in processed foods. But even though the quantities used are very small, they can still be very painful for the arthritic.

It is far better to use natural flavour, such as a vanilla pod rather than the essence, and, of course, to avoid all ready prepared foods which nearly always have some additives. This may take a little more time but, firstly, you will not find life so painful and, secondly, you will begin to realize what the real thing tastes like again.

One other additive you may find mentioned on a packet label, along with flavour, is solvent. These solvents are used to carry the flavour right through the food and, like the flavourings, are best avoided.

Today, new sources of foods are being found and produced. One in particular is Textured Vegetable Protein (TVP), and this will become increasingly used over the next few years to provide a good, nutritious and reasonably priced food for the world's population. To make the TVP more acceptable, colourings and flavourings will be used. When the arthritic wants to use TVP, it is most important that the basic commodity is found and used and flavoured only by yeast extract, vegetable or chicken stock. Two of the most widely used flavourings for processed TVP are monosodium glutamate and hydrolysed protein; these must be avoided.

Additives in bread and flour

In the section dealing with the breads and flours you may eat the various methods of bread-making are mentioned so that you can choose bread which is additive-free. But it is quite interesting to note just what additives are put into our flours for bread-making and the reasons why they are used.

To start with, there are five different yeast-stimulating preparations. These are mineral salts and they make the yeast grow more quickly and cut out much of the time in bread-making. These include ammonium chloride and calcium sulphate. Next come added enzymes, usually malt flour, soya flour or amylases, and these standardize variations in the different flours, so that the standard loaf can be reproduced time and time again.

An emulsifier is added to the flour in the form of lecithin, and ascorbic acid is used as a preservative. The preservative prevents the growth of mould in the bread and this of course means that the bread has a greater shelf life and the consumer no longer finds it necessary to shop every day for her fresh loaf, as she did in the past.

Brown colouring is sometimes added to brown breads, but the term brown bread should not be confused with wholemeal bread which is, of course, protected from all additives. Starch is also added. This is an excipient which means that it enables all the other additives to mix into the dough more easily and thoroughly.

Bread can develop brown spots in the middle of the loaf, and this is known as 'rope'. When this develops, the loaf will start to turn brown and can be pulled into rope-like threads. To prevent this happening, acids are added, usually vinegar, lactic acid or sodium diacetate. Finally, any fats used in the bread-making contain antioxidants, which make for yet another additive to your usual wrapped, sliced standard loaf.

A formidable list, but every additive mentioned is permitted by the government and widely used. Maybe this will give you a few reasons as to why making your own bread should become more attractive. It must, of course, be stressed that in normal health none of these additives is harmful, but it has been shown that arthritics who change the bread and flour they eat, from the commercial ones to those which are free from additives, have found great benefit.

Additives in animal feedstuffs

Over the past twenty years additives have been used in the feedstuffs of animals to improve their growth rate or milk yield, and also to allow large numbers of animals to be kept on a small amount of land. This is called intensive farming. Because of the risk of infection, antibiotics were also included in the feeds. All this means that a large concentration of additives and antibiotics get passed on to the consumer. The use of antibiotics has now been stopped, except in specific instances on the advice of a vet, but the other additives are still used. This not only applies to cattle and pigs, it also happens when chickens are intensively farmed for the frozen chicken market. It is because of this that it is better to buy free-range chickens which are fed naturally and cannot pass on to you additives which could make your condition worse. Not only that, they taste better too.

Pesticides

Unfortunately, pesticides are a fact of life. They are absolutely necessary to prevent attack on crops by fungi, insects, bacteria and viruses. Without these pesticides farmers would produce far less grain and other crops, and we would starve.

I suppose the answer is to grow your own vegetables and grain and only use organic fertilizers, an answer which is impracticable for the vast majority of people.

We will inevitably get traces of pesticides in our food, but the less we get the better. It is best to buy organically grown vegetables if possible, and make sure that any vegetables you buy are washed well before preparation.

This section on food additives is by no means extensive, and the interested person can find plenty of books on the subject in the local library. But the overall lesson can be learned from these few brief notes. Food additives are around and there will be more of them in the future, and it is a fact of life that they will come our way whether we want them to or not. But, and this is the big point, we can, to quite a large extent, control the amount of them we eat. A little longer spent in the kitchen is inevitable I'm afraid, but the bonus will be in the food, which will taste so much nicer, and be better for you.

Basic Nutrition

Anyone on a new diet is bound to question whether, after changing their eating habits, they will still receive a balanced diet.

Firstly, what is meant by a balanced diet?

Essentially, a balanced diet is one which contains sufficient quantities of nutrients to maintain body functions, repair body tissue and provide sufficient energy. We usually associate a poorly balanced diet with deficiency diseases such as scurvy and pellagra, rickets and beriberi, but fortunately today these diseases are relatively rare. Even so, it does not follow that we are all receiving a correctly balanced diet just because these diseases are not seen very often. Today there are plenty of diseases of malnutrition around for us all to see. Obesity and heart disease, gall stones and constipation, and of course dental caries.

A diet which provides the body with too much energy food, which that person does not use, results in fat. The body cannot use all the excess energy it has absorbed, so it lays down the excess as fat, in the expectation that during a lean period this fat can be withdrawn and used. Of course we all know that this lean period rarely happens, unless we really limit our intake of food and go on a slimming diet. Just a thought, one extra knob of margarine consumed but not used by the body every day for twenty years, can store up six extra stones, often described as 'middle age spread'. Thus a balanced diet must provide just sufficient nutrient, not too much and not too little.

Our daily diet must contain protein for body building, carbohydrate for fibre and bulk, and fat for energy, plus vitamins and minerals which are essential if all our bodily functions are to operate smoothly. Research has shown just how much of each group is needed to provide a balanced diet for the average person, in the number of milligrams of vitamins and proteins and micrograms of minerals. Of course, one doesn't measure these out, as no one has the facilities at home to do this, but there are guide lines to follow and these will be discussed.

To simplify matters we can place the essential foods into four groups. Portions should be served from each group every day.

Group 1: Fish, egg whites, pulses (such as peas, soya beans, lentils, etc.) and nuts

This group contains the main protein foods. Two portions should be served every day.

Group 2: Vegetables and potatoes

These contain protein, carbohydrate and fibre and two to three portions of these should be chosen every day, one of which should be green. The fresher the vegetable, the greater the nutrient available.

Group 3: Cereals

These provide energy in the diet, plus a certain amount of extra protein and, of course, fibre if the cereal chosen is the whole grain and not greatly refined. The amount needed will depend on appetite and the work done each day, but you should aim to feel satisfied but not bloated after a meal, and you should maintain your body weight once you have reached the correct weight for your age, build and height.

Group 4: Fats

These include margarine and vegetable oils. They should be taken every day, but in moderation, because although they provide vitamins A, D and E they do have a high calorific value which provides energy. Again, too much unused margarine or oil is laid down in the body, and makes for unwanted fat.

In spite of some improvement in recent years, the Western diet is still unbalanced. Although it includes food from all four groups, the proportions are incorrect. For example, most people eat a diet that is too high in animal fat and too low in carbohydrates. Changing to the Dong Diet would be a beneficial step for most people, not just the arthritic, because, apart from the very low percentage of fat in fish and chicken breast, there is NO animal fat in the diet.

Read any book about special diets for heart condition, obesity or high cholesterol, and the same advice is given: cut out red meat and increase the amount of vegetables consumed. This advice, coupled with eating starchy products such as bread and rice, should redress the poor balance of carbohydrates.

Fat, in the form of either margarine or vegetable oil, or hidden in foods such as fish, chicken, bread, soya milk, etc. should not exceed more than 30% of the total calories consumed daily. Bearing in mind that 25 g (1 oz) fat produces 225 calories, whereas the same weight of bread produces 65, of fish 20, and of vegetables only 5–10 calories, it is not difficult to see that a little fat goes a long, long way in a correctly balanced diet roughly composed of:

11%	protein	(fish, chicken, vegetables, soya products)
30%	fat	(hidden in the protein, in vegetable oil, bread, margarine)
55%	carbohydrates	(bread, rice, etc.)

There is no need to get too technical and work out your diet to the last gram of calorific value. To start with, it would take ages and, furthermore, it would probably make you paranoid. However, do look at your dinner plate – are there far more vegetables, potatoes, rice, etc. than there is fish or chicken? If not, then think very seriously about cutting back on the protein and bulking out on the vegetables. This will automatically cause a shift in the fat balance as well.

By eating foods from all four groups, plus keeping an eye on the balance of foods, a truly 'balanced diet' will result.

But certain circumstances must be taken into account which vary this pattern slightly. Women of childbearing years do require more iron than is usually obtained in the diet; therefore, more fatty fish should be eaten, or an iron supplement taken. During pregnancy and lactation extra nutrients are needed to feed the growing child. Extra protein is especially necessary and this will come from extra fish, soya products and vegetables. Please note – extra nutrients, not loads of extra calories. Extra vegetables and some whole cereals will give roughage and prevent constipation, often a side-effect of pregnancy.

Children and adolescents require more nutrients in proportion to their size, and again this should be protein and vegetable food, not loads of stodge obtained from processed foods.

Lastly, a group of people who also have special dietary needs are the elderly. They need the same amount of nutrients, but do not require much energy. Tinned fish and vegetables and soya milk provide easily prepared and chewed foods which give all the essential proteins, minerals and vitamins. But some extra vitamin D may be needed. Most people are able to synthesize much of their vitamin D from sunlight on their skin, but in the case of the elderly who rarely go out, this may not be the case, so that their bones become brittle and break easily. Cod liver oil can be a very useful additive here.

Having talked about a balanced diet, we can now break down each group to see just what it does for us and why it is necessary to keep our bodies functioning efficiently.

Protein

We all need protein every day. Our bodies are made up of millions of cells, and each one of these contains some protein. Every day, some of these cells die and they have to be replaced with new cells containing new protein. And so, to enable these new cells to be made, we must eat sufficient quantities of protein each day.

There are no natural foods which are 100% protein, but most of the foods we eat do contain small amounts, notable exceptions being fat, sugar and alcohol, which contain no protein at all.

Proteins are very complex and are made up of strings of amino-acids, each protein food containing different groupings of these acids. Animal proteins, like those in fish, egg whites and chicken breast, contain all the essential amino-acids needed to rebuild new cells, whereas vegetable proteins usually have one or two of the essential amino-acids missing, therefore they are not complete in themselves. But this does not make them second class, because by eating a good selection of different vegetables and cereals, the protein balance of all the essential amino-acids will be achieved.

Most adults eat about 65 g ($2\frac{1}{2}$ oz) of protein a day, although the minimum requirement is only about 40–50 g ($1\frac{1}{2}$–2 oz). To ensure that our bodies do get all the protein needed, the recommended amount varies between 50–75 g (2–3 oz) per day (according to a person's size in terms of muscle and bone, not fat, because fat contains no protein). Growing children and expectant women also require the top amount of protein because their bodies are creating new cells at a greater speed than normal.

For our bodies to utilize all the protein we eat, carbohydrate should be eaten at the same time; for example, a piece of fish eaten on its own would not give your body as much of its available protein as it would if chips were served at the same meal. The carbohydrate from the potatoes helps the body to utilize all the protein from the fish.

If a high-protein diet is eaten, then the protein not used for body-building is turned into glucose and fat and is used for energy. Thus a high-protein diet consumed by a sedentary person could still make that person fat, because any other food consumed would be surplus to the energy requirements of the body. The body would use the minerals and vitamins and then just lay down the rest in fat. So it is important to get the balance of protein and carbohydrate right for your needs.

Below is a list of the grams of protein in an average portion of food, to give you a guide as to how much you need every day.

source	protein content
100 g (4 oz) white fish	18 g
50 g (2 oz) nuts	14 g
150 g (6 oz) potatoes	2 g
3 slices (4 oz) bread	8 g
50 g (2 oz) spun soya	14 g
50 g (2 oz) tinned salmon	11 g
250 ml (½ pt) diluted soya milk	9 g

Carbohydrate

When we refer to carbohydrate in a diet, we really mean the sugar and starches found in foods. Both these groups contain the same amount of energy, which is about 4 calories per gram.

Sugar and refined starches are the most concentrated sources of carbohydrate available, but they are composed purely of carbohydrate and nothing else, so they are plain and simple energy foods and can be left out of the diet without causing any dietary deficiency.

The other sources of carbohydrate, such as flour, bread, cakes, biscuits, breakfast cereals, pastry, honey, potatoes, vegetables and nuts are far preferable in a diet because they all contain other nutrients as well. If you cut out all carbohydrate from your daily food, you would also lose other very valuable nutrients as well; a good example is the vitamin C in potatoes and another is the protein and vitamin B complex in flour.

The carbohydrate in our diet is very important, as without it we would have difficulty in maintaining our body weight, and we would have very little energy to do our daily work. Too much carbohydrate not used up in work during the day will get laid down by the body as fat.

Apart from the energy it gives us, carbohydrate has other important jobs. To obtain the maximum protein from our food, our metabolism requires some carbohydrate to assimilate that protein, so we need it as a kind of catalyst. This is one of the reasons why we should never cut out carbohydrates altogether from a diet if trying to lose weight.

The best way to get a good balanced diet is to eat the unrefined carbohydrates of wholemeal bread, brown rice and potatoes, along with the rich protein foods like fish, nuts and soya products. And it is just as important to eat sufficient quantities to feel satisfied but not over full.

Fat

Fat is present in many of the foods we eat, but within Dr Dong's diet all the fat eaten must be of vegetable origin, and as most fats from this source are liquid at normal temperatures they are usually called oils. These oils are high in polyunsaturated fatty acids which are better for you as they do not become laid down in the arteries as cholesterol.

Fats and oils provide energy for the body to move and keep warm, and all fats and oils have the same calorific value, so none are more slimming than others.

Apart from their use in providing energy (weight for weight they provide more than carbohydrate), they also contain the fat soluble vitamins A and D, which are essential for the correct functioning of certain body processes.

An average diet should supply about 120 g of fat to the body per day and this will supply about half of the energy needs. A very low fat diet is very unpalatable, because many flavours are dissolved in the fat content of the food. Also the texture is more pleasing when a little fat is present, as it helps to lubricate the food and make it easier to swallow. Finally, fat in food prolongs the time the food remains in the stomach, therefore one feels more satisfied for longer. Of course, a food that is too fatty may cause indigestion because it remains in the stomach for too long.

The table below shows how much fat is obtained from an average portion of certain foods.

source	fat content
25 g (1 oz) vegetable oil	25 g
25 g (1 oz) margarine	25 g
100 g (4 oz) chicken breast	8 g
100 g (4 oz) herrings	14 g
3 slices (4 oz) wholemeal bread	1 g
50 g (2 oz) nuts	28 g
25 g (1 oz) soya flour	6.5 g

Vegetables and honey do not contain any fat at all.

Vitamins

Vitamin A

Vitamin A is essential to maintain healthy skin. It is also necessary to prevent night and colour blindness, and is probably involved in the senses of taste and balance. The quantity recommended for each day is 750 milligrams, but this probably far exceeds the minimum required. Deficiency is fairly uncommon in Great Britain, but in underdeveloped countries, such as India, it is estimated that 10,000 children go blind every year from a lack of vitamin A. An early sign of deficiency is night blindness, and as carrots contain vitamin A, the old saying that carrots help you see in the dark is not so far from the truth.

A very rich source of vitamin A is liver, but even though this is not allowed on this diet, there is still not too much fear of vitamin A deficiency. A daily portion of dark green vegetables or carrots would provide an adequate supply. Margarine, chicken and fatty fish are also good sources. Your body can store a certain amount of vitamin A, and so it is not likely to be necessary to take a vitamin A supplement. If you were to you'd need medical supervision, as too much vitamin A can be toxic.

One of the good things about vitamin A, when it comes to cooking, is that it is very stable in heat, and, being fat soluble, it does not leak out into the cooking water. However, vitamin A is destroyed when fat goes rancid, which is why margarine contains antioxidants to prevent this occurring. The table below shows the amount of certain foods which give a day's supply.

One day's supply vitamin A

source	amount
chicken	15 g ($\frac{1}{2}$ oz)
old carrots	40 g ($1\frac{1}{2}$ oz)
new carrots	75 g (3 oz)
spinach	75 g (3 oz)
margarine	75 g (3 oz)
broccoli	150 g (6 oz)

Vitamin B complex

All the different B vitamins, except B_{12}, are found in yeasts and their extracts, cereal germ and many other foods. Vitamin B_{12} is only found in animal food. Eight of the B complex vitamins are known to be essential nutrients and, although differing in chemical structure, they control related functions in the body.

Vitamin B_1 (thiamine)

Thiamine in the diet is essential for growth and life, and a lack of this vitamin would result in beriberi and other nervous disorders.

Vitamin B_1 is water soluble and is found in yeast, wholegrain cereals, cod's roe, nuts, peas, beans, and also in small amounts in many other foods. A balanced diet will provide all the vitamin B the body requires.

Thiamine is essential for the nervous system and for helping the protein to do its work. Only small amounts of thiamine are required by the body; one milligram is considered to be sufficient. Men require slightly more than women, as they are larger and need more protein in the body to produce more cells.

Thiamine cannot be stored in the body, and any excess over and above the daily requirement is filtered out of the blood system by the kidneys. Pills and tonics which are taken as a supplement are usually of no value, and a balanced diet is far the best way of obtaining the small amounts the body needs.

One day's supply vitamin B_1

source	amount
yeast	7 g ($\frac{1}{4}$ oz)
cod's roe	65 g ($2\frac{1}{2}$ oz)
wheat germ	50 g (2 oz)
Brazil nuts	90 g ($3\frac{1}{2}$ oz)
fresh peanuts	100 g (4 oz)
wholewheat flour	200 g (7 oz)
peas	300 g (11 oz)

Vitamin B_2 (riboflavin)

Riboflavin is required for growth in children and for maintaining healthy skin and eyes. It is present in small amounts in most foods except sugar and fat, and deficiencies are unlikely. About 1.8 milligrams are needed each day, and as the vitamin is so widespread, this can easily be obtained.

Yeast is a particularly good source, as are eggs, mackerel, fish roes, mushrooms and enriched breakfast cereals. Moderate amounts are found in wholemeal bread, other fish, nuts, dark green vegetables, avocado pears, and all vegetables contain traces.

Riboflavin is fairly stable in heat, but being water soluble it does leak out into cooking water, which explains why it is a good thing to use the cooking water for sauces, soups and gravies.

Deficiency of this vitamin is rare because a diet lacking in riboflavin would be lacking in all the other B complex vitamins. A lack of riboflavin in children checks the growth rate, but in adults it does not appear to have a very serious effect; a sore tongue, bloodshot or itchy eyes may result, however, these symptoms could be due to other causes. Extra intake of riboflavin in the form of pills and tonics is usually a waste as the body does not store this vitamin, and any excess is filtered out of the blood-stream by the kidneys. A balanced diet (including for the elderly 285 ml (10 fl oz) soya milk each day) would give the body all it needs.

One day's supply vitamin B_2

source	amount
sardines	300 g (11 oz)
mackerel	300 g (11 oz)
herrings	300 g (11 oz)
wholewheat flour	300 g (11 oz)
wheat bran	150 g (6 oz)
almonds	150 g (6 oz)

Vitamin B_3 (nicotinic acid)

A lack of nicotinic acid in the body produces a disease called pellagra. There is no store in the body, but it is distributed throughout the cells and a diet lacking in nicotinic acid would take about fifty days to deplete the supply from the body tissues.

The amino-acid tryptophan, which is present in most protein foods, can be converted into nicotinic acid by the liver, when there are sufficient quantities of vitamins B_1, B_2 and B_3 available. Sometimes one reads in vitamin tables of nicotinic acid equivalents. These are the quantities of the other vitamins needed to allow the body to manufacture the required amount of nicotinic acid.

Most foods contain some nicotinic acid equivalents (except sugar, fat and alcohol), however, the rich protein foods such as yeast extract, peanuts, fish, pulses, egg whites, vegetables and wholemeal bread provide the largest supply. Nicotinic acid is very stable and is unaffected by heat or processing. It is water soluble, but remember it can be recovered by using the cooking water for gravies, etc.

Again, a well-balanced diet supplies all the daily need of nicotinic acid or its equivalent and 15 milligrams per day is perfectly adequate.

One day's supply vitamin B_3 (nicotinic acid)

source	amount
peanuts	100 g (4 oz)
mushrooms	450 g (16 oz)
halibut	150 g (6 oz)
mackerel	225 g (8 oz)
sardines	225 g (8 oz)
salmon	200 g (7 oz)

Vitamin B_6 (pyridoxine)

This is another vitamin which is essential for growth. When digested it helps the body to form new protein cells from the amino-acids taken from protein foods. It is also important in blood formation, protection against infection, healthy skin and nerves.

Good sources, as for all other B complex vitamins, are yeast extracts, mackerel and other fish, soya milk and wholemeal bread. Once again, a deficiency is rare if a balanced diet is eaten every day.

There is no specific disease attributed to a lack of vitamin B_6, and only 1–1.5 milligrams is needed daily. An average amount of 1–2 milligrams consumed every day is thought to be sufficient to maintain good health.

One day's supply vitamin B_6

source	amount
chicken	200 g (7 oz)
avocado	200 g (2 whole avocados)
yeast	50 g (2 oz)
wheat germ	25 g (1 oz)

Vitamin B₁₂

This part of the vitamin B complex contains cobalt which is necessary for the formation of red blood corpuscles so it protects against pernicious anaemia and lesions in the nervous system. It comes largely from animal foods and is entirely absent from all plants. So, with Dr Dong's diet, fatty fish, shell fish, white fish and egg whites should be eaten regularly as these will be your only supply of this vitamin.

Like all other vitamins from the vitamin B complex, all of which are essential nutrients, B_{12} is only needed in small quantities – 2–3 micrograms a day is sufficient. A microgram is a millionth of a gram, which is a very small amount but vital none the less.

It is very stable in heat, but like all its fellows in the complex it is water soluble, so it can leak out into cooking water, but remember this can all be reclaimed by using the cooking water to make a sauce, soup, or even as a drink.

One day's supply vitamin B₁₂

source	amount
sardines	25 g (1 oz)
pilchards	25 g (1 oz)
herrings	25 g (1 oz)
brisling	25 g (1 oz)
tuna fish	90 g (3½ oz)
salmon	90 g (3½ oz)
egg white	90 g (3½ oz)

Unlike the other B vitamins, B_{12} is stored in the liver, and this provides most people with about a two-year supply. However, if over a long period a diet is lacking in B_{12}, this store will be used up and pernicious anaemia can result.

Folic acid

An insufficiency of folic acid in the diet can result in anaemia. However, our bodies do keep a three- to four-month store in the liver, so the onset of anaemia would be a gradual thing, and care should be taken to keep that store 'topped up'. Our best supply of folic acid comes from yeast extracts, nuts, dark green vegetables and wholegrain cereals. Once again, a well-balanced diet would ensure a sufficient supply for our needs.

Adults need 100–200 micrograms per day, not a great amount but vital, because it is used by the body in the complicated process of making new cells.

All foods contain small amounts of folic acid (except fat, sugar and alcohol), but it is very unstable. It is sensitive to light, heat and oxygen and will also leak into cooking water; so although green vegetables are a good source of folic acid, nearly 90% can be lost if the vegetables are stale, badly cooked, and then not served immediately. The section on vitamin C (below) gives all the rules for cooking vegetables to maintain the maximum nutritious content including folic acid. But always remember that a diet containing a good variety of foods, well cooked, will ensure a day's supply.

Biotin and pantothenic acid

These last two essential vitamins in the vitamin B complex are very widespread in food (the exceptions are sugar, fat and alcohol) and deficiency is unknown except as a result of certain experimental diets. Very small amounts are needed for correct metabolism, and in a diet such as Dr Dong's, these amounts are available without any problem.

Vitamin C (ascorbic acid)

Small amounts of vitamin C are essential for growth, however, this requirement should be increased during recovery from severe accident or surgery. It has been said in the past that a large supply of vitamin C builds up a resistance to infection, but this is now debatable. Nevertheless, total lack of vitamin C can cause scurvy which results in swollen gums, skin sores, tiredness and depression.

In a normal British diet about a quarter of a day's requirement of vitamin C is obtained from potatoes, a quarter from other vegetables and about a third from fruit.

In a diet such as this, in which fruit is not allowed, the whole requirement – about 30 milligrams of vitamin C per day for adults – must come from vegetable sources.

One day's supply vitamin C

source	amount
watercress	15 g (½ oz)
mustard and cress	15 g (½ oz)
green pepper	25 g (1 oz)
parsley	25 g (1 oz)
raw cabbage	225 g (8 oz)
avocado pears	225–325 g (8–12 oz)
spring onions	225–325 g (8–12 oz)
radishes	225–325 g (8–12 oz)
lettuce	225–325 g (8–12 oz)
celery	225–325 g (8–12 oz)

All the above vegetables should be eaten raw

source	amount (raw weight)
broccoli spears	25 g (1 oz)
Brussels sprouts	25 g (1 oz)
cauliflower	40 g (1½ oz)
kale	25 g (1 oz)
asparagus	100 g (4 oz)
spinach	100 g (4 oz)
new potatoes	100 g (4 oz)
runner beans	225–325 g (8–12 oz)
leeks	225–325 g (8–12 oz)
old potatoes	225–325 g (8–12 oz)
peas	225–325 g (8–12 oz)
swedes	225–325 g (8–12 oz)
parsnips	225–325 g (8–12 oz)

All the above vegetables should be boiled in the minimum amount of water and eaten immediately

Obviously, a 225 g (8 oz) portion of lettuce or spring onions is hardly likely in a meal, but these quantities give some guide as to where most vitamin C is found, and gives scope for balancing one good source with another not so good in order to get a full day's requirement.

The choice of vegetables is important. Whether or not they contain all the vitamin C they should is dependent on many factors; these are worth knowing about.

The greatest loss of vitamin C occurs during storage, and further loss takes place during preparation and cooking. As a general rule, the fresher the vegetable the greater the vitamin C content. Growing your own vegetables is without doubt the best way of ensuring the maximum vitamin C content, but this is not always practical. Do not shun frozen vegetables, because they are frozen as soon after harvest as possible and are often higher in vitamin C content than vegetables bought in the local market, and are certainly better than those bought on Friday and eaten the following week.

Preparation, namely cutting, is the next stage where vitamin C is lost. When a vegetable is cut, an enzyme is released which oxidizes the vitamin C, so the less you cut them the better. For example, potatoes are best cooked in their skins, and then the skins removed after cooking, so as to keep the loss to a minimum.

The greatest loss of vitamin C occurs during cooking. Vitamin C is water soluble, so quite a lot is lost into the cooking water. To minimize this, cook the vegetables in a small amount of water, or even steam them. Cook for the minimum time and use the vegetable water in soups or sauces, or for vegetable cocktail drinks.

Lastly, eat the vegetables as soon as possible after cooking, this is because the vitamin C that you have worked to preserve will be gradually destroyed by heat in the time that the dish spends on the hot plate. Very often canteen vegetables are completely without vitamin C by the time they reach your plate.

All this might seem to suggest that to get any vitamin C at all is a bit of a miracle, but 30 milligrams is not that much and with a little care and thought that requirement can be met very easily.

Vitamin D

There are two sources of vitamin D used by the body. Firstly, it can be obtained from the food we eat; and secondly, it can be formed by sunlight acting upon the skin.

It is important to have a sufficient supply of vitamin D because it is necessary to enable the body to absorb the calcium from our food, and this in turn is used to harden bones. A lack of vitamin D causes rickets in children and osteomalacia in adults.

Unfortunately, vitamin D is not found in many foods, but two main sources, fatty fish and margarine, are foods allowed by Dr Dong's diet. However, it is advised that during pregnancy and lactation a supplement is taken, because during this time calcium is withdrawn from the body to give to the growing child, and a deficiency could occur within the mother. Also, more vitamin D is needed during childhood, when bones and teeth are being formed in large quantities. In these cases, cod liver oil and malt are recommended additives. But, if a child is active and spends lots of time outdoors, then the extra vitamin D needed would be obtained from the sunlight.

Elderly people, who do not go out very much, are also at risk from a lack of vitamin D, and this is often the reason why elderly people sustain broken bones after only a slight fall. Again, a supplement in the form of cod liver oil can be very useful to prevent any likelihood of deficiency.

Excessive vitamin D is toxic. Too much vitamin D causes too much calcium to be absorbed from food and this leads to a high level of calcium in the blood-stream. Thus, it is most important that supplements are only taken when prescribed by a doctor, and then only the recommended dose.

The daily amount of vitamin D recommended for an adult is 2.5 micrograms and the amounts of foods below will provide a day's supply for an active adult.

One day's supply vitamin D

source	amount
cod liver oil	1 teaspoon
herrings	100 g (4 oz)
salmon	200 g (7 oz)
sardines	325 g (12 oz)
cod liver oil and malt	1 dessertspoon
margarine	40 g (1½ oz)

Vitamin E

Nearly all foods contain a small amount of vitamin E and because of this, deficiency is rare. It is a fat soluble vitamin and is found in fatty foods, and vegetable oils.

It is also a very stable vitamin, and only very small amounts are lost during cooking, processing and storage. However, oil which is repeatedly used for frying will lose all its vitamin E content.

Vitamin K

Without vitamin K, the protein which is responsible for the clotting of blood would not be formed; thus a deficiency could cause prolonged bleeding. The body is not dependent entirely for its vitamin K on a dietary source, because about half the daily supply is synthesized by bacteria lining the digestive system.

Vitamin K is fat soluble, but surprisingly, most vitamin K in the diet comes from vegetables; most other foods have none at all.

A daily requirement for an adult is about 100 micrograms, and this can easily be obtained from one helping of vegetables. It is also a very stable vitamin. It is only affected a little by heat, and being fat soluble it does not leak out into the cooking water.

Minerals

Minerals are essential in our diet. About eighteen are known to be necessary, and they all have different jobs to do to keep the body functions working correctly. Of these eighteen, seven, which are calcium, iron, magnesium, chlorine, phosphorus, sodium and sulphur, are found in relatively large quantities throughout our foods. The other eleven, which are required as trace elements and include iodine, manganese, nickel, copper, zinc, tin and chromium, are all easily found in the small quantities required, and a balanced diet is unlikely to show any deficiency.

Calorie Control

Many people suffering from osteoarthritis are advised by their doctors to lose weight, because any excess weight causes painful pressure on already damaged joints.

For the arthritic sufferer with this extra problem, changing from a diet containing meat and dairy produce to a fish and vegetable diet initially causes a loss of weight, due to a loss of all animal fat. This alone is a cut back in calories, and will help with weight loss. Beyond that, of course, it is up to the individual concerned to govern the foods eaten every day, so that an ideal weight will be maintained.

A calorie is a unit of heat, and is used in the body as energy, to move, keep warm and maintain body functions such as breathing and digestion. Calories are being used all the time, both day and night, but the more energy expended the more calories used; so obviously a game of tennis uses up more calories than a night's sleep. But even when you are asleep calories are still being used to keep your heart beating and blood circulating.

A simple equation is necessary to the understanding of body weight:

CALORIES USED = ENERGY USED

Take in more calories than you are using and you will get fat; use more energy than you supply, by your intake of food, and you will get thin. Simple in theory and in most cases absolutely true. There are the odd cases which defy this theory, and research is going on into the problem, but for the vast majority of people, too much food makes you fat and too little makes you thin, and an even balance maintains your body weight. Simple, yes. But how are you to go about it?

The answer is to learn the calorific value of the foods you eat, and to know how many calories you require each day.

There are some tables at the end of this chapter which will give you a guide for the ideal body weight for your sex, age, and build. Of course, as good a guide as any is a full-length mirror and a good long honest look at the spare tyres (if there are any).

Thus, armed with a calorie chart, a basic knowledge of simple arithmetic, and a pair of scales, you have all you need to regulate your diet.

For those who want to lose weight it is best to go easy on the rice and bread, but not to cut them out completely, as they are a good food source; to use oil sparingly in your cooking; and above all, to avoid all the empty calories in sugar. On the other hand, if you could do with a bit of extra padding, be liberal with oil in cooking, eat bread and rice with your meals, and try to increase the amount of protein you eat; all this will help to produce your ideal weight.

Of course it is absolutely maddening when you meet people who seem to eat like horses, yet remain thin and light. But we are all different, and some people's metabolism is more efficient than others', so that they are able to burn off excess calories more easily. You are stuck with your basic metabolic rate, but even so, there is no need to allow the weight situation to get out of hand.

In the charts beginning on page 234 the food values are given as calories. When we talk of a calorie, we do in fact mean a kilocalorie, as a calorie is such a small unit, but a kilocalorie is usually abbreviated to the letter C. The number of kilocalories needed by a moderately active female is about 2500 C.

Increasingly, the kilocalorie is being replaced by the kilojoule. The reason for this is a result of the adoption by Great Britain of the international system of units, which will eventually make all units standard, as the metric system is doing. It is best to introduce it here, as it will become more and more common as time goes on, but at the moment it is only used in a scientific context. There are 4.2 joules in every calorie; thus to obtain the number of joules in a certain food, you must multiply the number of calories by 4.2.

The following tables should only be used as a guide for your ideal weight, and the number of calories you require each day. Everybody differs in make up, bone size, build and activities. So there are no hard and fast rules to obey. But these tables should be used as a rough guide.

Approximate number of calories/joules required each day

age	calories	joules
women		
11–14	2400	10080
15–22	2100	8820
23–50	2000	8400
over 50	1800	7560
pregnant women	2400	10080
lactating women	2600	10920
men		
11–14	2800	11760
15–22	3000	12600
23–50	2700	11340
over 50	1800	7560

Table of recommended weight at 25 years of age
(Deduct .45 kg (1 lb) for every year under 25)

women

height			small frame			medium frame			large frame		
ft	in	cm	st	lb	kg	st	lb	kg	st	lb	kg
4	10	147.5	6	11	43	7	3	46	7	13	50.5
4	11	150	6	13	44	7	6	47	8	2	52
5	0	152.5	7	2	45.5	7	9	48.5	8	5	53
5	1	155	7	5	47	7	12	50	8	8	54.5
5	2	157.5	7	8	48	8	1	51	8	11	56
5	3	160	7	11	49.5	8	4	52.5	9	0	57
5	4	162.5	8	0	51	8	7	54	9	3	58.5
5	5	165	8	4	52.5	8	11	56	9	7	60
5	6	167.5	8	6	53.5	9	1	57.5	9	11	62
5	7	170	8	10	55	9	5	59.5	10	1	64
5	8	172.5	9	0	57	9	9	61	10	5	66
5	9	175	9	4	59	9	13	63	10	9	67.5
5	10	177.5	9	9	61	10	3	65	11	0	70
5	11	180	9	13	63	10	7	67	11	4	71.5
6	0	182.5	10	5	66	10	11	68.5	11	9	74

men

height			small frame			medium frame			large frame		
ft	in	cm	st	lb	kg	st	lb	kg	st	lb	kg
5	2	157.5	8	4	52.5	8	11	56	9	7	60
5	3	160	8	7	54	9	1	57.5	9	10	61.5
5	4	162.5	8	10	55	9	4	59	10	0	63.5
5	5	165	8	13	57	9	7	60	10	3	65
5	6	167.5	9	2	58	9	10	61.5	10	7	67
5	7	170	9	6	59.5	10	0	63.5	10	11	68.5
5	8	172.5	9	10	61.5	10	5	66	11	2	70.5
5	9	175	10	0	63.5	10	9	67.5	11	6	72.5
5	10	177.5	10	5	66	10	13	69	11	10	74
5	11	180	10	9	67.5	11	3	71	12	1	76.5
6	0	182.5	10	13	69	11	8	73	12	6	79
6	1	185	11	3	71	11	12	75	12	10	80.5
6	2	187.5	11	7	73	12	3	77.5	13	1	83
6	3	190	11	11	75	12	8	80	13	6	85
6	4	192.5	12	1	76.5	12	13	82	13	11	88

Number of calories in foods allowed within Dr Dong's diet

food	calories per 100 g	per oz	joules per 100g	per oz
almonds, shelled	598	170	2512	714
anchovies	141	40	592	168
arrowroot	355	101	1491	428
artichokes, globe, boiled	7	2	29	8
artichokes, Jerusalem, boiled	19	5	80	21
asparagus, boiled	9	3	38	13
asparagus, tinned or frozen	18	5	80	21
aubergine, raw	15	4	63	17
avocado pear, weighed without stone	88	25	370	105
barley, pearl, raw	360	102	1512	428
barley, pearl, boiled	120	34	504	143
bass, steamed, weighed with bones	67	19	281	80
beans, broad, boiled	43	12	181	50
beans, butter, boiled	93	26	391	109
beans, French, boiled	7	2	29	9
beans, haricot, boiled	89	25	374	105
beans, runner, boiled	7	2	29	9
beans, soya	130	35	546	147
beetroot, boiled	44	13	185	55
Brazil nuts, weighed with shells	289	82	1214	344
bread	228	65	958	273
bream, steamed, weighed with bones	66	19	277	80
brill, steamed, weighed with bones	78	22	328	92
broccoli, boiled	14	4	59	17
Brussels sprouts, raw	32	9	134	38
Brussels sprouts, boiled	16	5	67	21
cabbage, red, raw	20	6	84	25
cabbage, savoy, boiled	9	3	38	13
cabbage, spring, boiled	8	2	34	8
carrots, raw	23	6	97	25
carrots, young, boiled	21	6	97	25
cauliflower, raw	25	7	105	29
cauliflower, boiled	11	3	46	13

food	calories per 100 g	per oz	joules per 100g	per oz
celeriac, boiled	14	4	59	17
celery, raw	9	3	38	13
celery, boiled	5	1	21	4
chestnuts, weighed in shells	141	40	592	168
chicken, boiled, weighed with bones	132	38	546	160
chicken, roast, weighed with bones	102	29	428	122
chicory, raw	9	3	38	13
cobnuts, weighed in shells	145	41	609	172
cockles	48	13	202	55
cod, steamed, weighed with skin and bones	66	19	277	80
cod's roe, fried	206	59	865	248
cod liver oil	930	264	3906	1109
coffee, black	0	0	0	0
corn on the cob	70	20	294	84
cornflour	354	100	1487	420
crab, boiled, weighed with shell	25	7	105	29
dabs, fried, weighed with bones	199	56	836	235
eggs, whites	39	11	164	46
endive, raw	11	3	46	13
flour, English, 100% wholemeal	333	95	1399	399
flour, English, 80%	348	99	1453	416
glucose, liquid BP	318	90	1336	378
haddock, fried, weighed with skin and bones	74	21	311	88
haddock, smoked, steamed, weighed with skin and bones	65	28	273	118
hake, fried, weighed with skin and bones	193	55	811	231
hake, steamed, weighed with skin and bones	86	24	361	101
halibut, steamed, weighed with skin and bones	99	28	416	118

food	calories per 100 g	per oz	joules per 100g	per oz
herring, fried, weighed with skin and bones	208	59	874	248
herring, baked, weighed with skin and bones	174	50	731	210
herring roe, fried	260	74	1092	311
honey	288	82	1210	344
honeycomb	281	80	1180	336
John Dory, steamed, weighed with skin and bones	59	17	248	71
kippers, grilled or baked, weighed with skin and bones	108	31	454	130
leeks, raw	30	9	126	38
leeks, boiled	25	7	105	29
lentils, boiled	96	27	403	122
lettuce, raw	11	3	46	13
macaroni, boiled	114	32	479	134
mackerel, fried, weighed with skin and bones	136	39	571	164
margarine	795	226	3339	949
marmite	6	2	25	8
marrow, boiled	7	2	29	8
mullet, red and grey, steamed, weighed with skin and bones	85	23	357	97
mushrooms, raw	7	2	29	8
mushrooms, fried	217	62	911	260
mussels, boiled	87	25	365	105
mussels, boiled, weighed in shells	26	7	109	29
mustard and cress, raw	10	3	42	13
Nescafé, black	0	0	0	0
oatmeal, raw	404	115	1697	438
olives, in brine, weighed with stones	85	24	357	101
olive oil	930	264	3906	1109
onions, raw	23	7	97	29
onions, boiled	13	4	55	17
onions, fried	355	101	1491	424

food	calories per 100 g	per oz	joules per 100g	per oz
onions, spring, raw	36	10	151	42
oysters, raw, in shells	6	2	25	8
parsley	21	6	88	25
parsnips, boiled	56	16	235	67
peanuts	603	171	2533	718
peanut butter	634	180	2663	756
peas, fresh, raw	64	18	269	76
peas, fresh, boiled	49	14	206	59
peas, dried, boiled	100	28	420	119
peas, split, dried, boiled	116	33	487	139
pilchards, tinned, drained of oil	191	54	802	227
plaice, steamed, weighed with skin and bones	50	14	210	59
popcorn	482	137	2024	575
potatoes, old, boiled	80	23	336	97
potatoes, old, jacket, weighed with skins	84	24	353	101
potatoes, old, roast	123	35	517	147
potatoes, old, chips	239	68	1004	286
potatoes, new, boiled	75	21	314	88
potato crisps, plain	559	159	2348	668
prawns	104	30	437	126
prawns, weighed in shells	40	11	168	46
rice, boiled	122	35	512	147
Ryvita	345	98	1449	412
sago	355	101	1491	424
salmon, fresh, steamed, weighed with skin and bones	161	57	676	239
salmon, tinned	137	39	575	164
salsify, boiled	18	5	76	21
salt, block and free-running	0	0	0	0
sardines, tinned in oil	294	84	1235	353
scallops, steamed, weighed without shells	105	30	441	126
scampi	299	85	1256	357
seakale (kale), boiled	8	2	37	8
shrimps	114	32	479	134

food	calories per 100 g	per oz	joules per 100g	per oz
skate, fried, weighed with bones	201	57	844	239
smelts, fried, weighed whole	346	98	1453	412
sole, steamed, weighed with skin and bones	50	14	210	59
sole, fried, weighed with skin and bones	241	68	1012	286
sole, lemon, steamed, weighed with skin and bones	64	18	267	76
sole, lemon, fried, weighed with skin and bones	173	49	727	206
soya, low-fat flour	335	95	1407	399
spaghetti	365	104	1533	437
spinach, boiled	26	7	109	29
sprats, fresh, fried, weighed whole	390	111	1638	466
sprats, smoked, grilled, weighed whole	284	81	1193	340
spring greens, boiled	10	3	42	13
sugar, demerara	394	112	1655	470
sugar, white	394	112	1655	470
swedes, boiled	18	5	76	21
sweet potatoes, boiled	80	23	336	97
syrup, golden	297	84	1247	353
tapioca	359	102	1508	428
tea, Indian, without milk	0	0	0	0
treacle, black	257	73	1079	307
trout, steamed, weighed with skin and bones	88	25	370	105
trout, sea, steamed, weighed with skin and bones	104	29	437	122
turbot, steamed, weighed with skin and bones	66	19	277	80
turnips, boiled	11	3	46	13
walnuts, shelled	549	156	2306	655
walnuts, with shells	352	100	1478	420
watercress, raw	15	4	63	17
Weetabix	351	100	1478	420

food	calories per 100 g	per oz	joules per 100g	per oz
whitebait, fried, weighed whole	537	152	2255	638
whiting, steamed, weighed with skin and bones	61	17	256	71
whiting, fried, weighed with skin and bones	174	49	731	206
winkles, boiled in salt or fresh water, weighed with shells	14	4	59	17

Alcoholic drinks allowed
Sauternes wine   130 calories/546 joules per glass
26 calories/109 joules per 30 ml (1 fl oz)
93 calories/391 joules per 100 ml (3.5 fl oz)
Irish rye whiskey 63 calories/265 joules per measure (⅙ gill)

Herbs and
Flavourings

In a diet which is as natural as possible herbs must surely play a part. In gardens or window boxes it is possible to grow a few little herb plants which, when added to your food, can make a tremendous difference to the taste of your everyday fare.

Fresh herbs are, without doubt, the best ones to use. Each one has its own special aroma and colour which is at its most delicate when fresh. Unfortunately, it is not always possible to grow your own. Nevertheless, the use of herbs is open to everyone because most grocery stores and supermarkets sell a good selection of dried herbs which can be used instead of fresh ones.

Dried herbs are sold in small jars because you do not need very much at a time and also because the shelf life of dried herbs is only about one year; after this time they begin to lose their aroma and pungency and will not give the same zing to a dish. In fact in many cases the taste can be far removed from the original fragrance of the fresh herb. Do be ruthless occasionally; throw out your old dried herbs and treat yourself to some new ones. The more you get used to using herbs in your cooking, the less likelihood there will be of having to throw some away.

The storage of dried herbs in your kitchen is most important. If you own one of those delightful herb racks which look so attractive, then fill the jars with old herbs and just admire them. The herbs you actually use are best kept in airtight jars in a cool dark place. A drawer some way away from the cooker is a good place; stored in this way the herbs will keep their aroma and colour much longer. When you buy dried herbs, buy them from a shop which specializes in herbs, or a shop where there is a good turnover of stock. Herbs can deteriorate just as easily in a shop as they can in your kitchen.

Incidentally, the same deterioration occurs in spices. Not very many spices are used within Dr Dong's diet, but cinnamon and nutmeg, which are occasionally recommended, have the same sort of shelf life as herbs and are best stored in the same way.

When you are using herbs or spices in your cooking, remember that subtlety is everything. A quarter or half a teaspoon of a dried herb, or half to one teaspoon of a fresh one should be added to a dish, and then the mellowing cooking processes should be allowed to take place; this will bring out the flavour of your chosen herb and mingle it with the rest of the ingredients. You should never be able to pick out the overpowering flavour of any particular herb. All you should be able to taste is a hint of that herb which will lift the meal from the ordinary to the delicious.

Therefore, go ahead and buy or, better still, grow, a few herbs and experiment with them in your kitchen, but always remember that too little of a herb flavour can be rectified; too much is a disaster.

Incidentally, dried herbs are twice as strong as fresh ones, and your own mixed herbs should contain half parsley and the other half made up of the herbs of your choice.

Herbs

Basil

Basil is an important culinary herb which can be grown from seed. To do really well it needs warm, sunny conditions, which is why long hot summers tend to give a better crop than others. However, many good supermarkets have supplies of fresh basil all the year round. Fresh leaves can be preserved by placing them in a dry jar with a pinch of salt and then covering them with olive oil.

The herb has a slightly peppery taste which can be useful as a pepper susbstitute since pepper is not on the diet. It is also the main ingredient of pesto – a fragrant mixture of basil, oil and pine kernels, ideal for serving with pasta. There is a recipe for making pesto in Part II.

Basil combines well with white fish, vegetable dishes and rice, as well as with pasta.

Bay

Bay leaves come from the aromatic bay tree which is really more of a shrub than a herb. The leaves of the bay tree are shiny green on top and a pale yellowish green underneath, and they can be picked all through the year. Fresh leaves are not as strong as the dried ones, so it is best to pick the leaves and dry them in a dark place so that they retain their natural colour and the aroma becomes stronger.

Bay leaves are best used in one piece, placed in the dish during the cooking time and then removed when the food is ready. They can be used for the flavouring in TVP dishes, as a part of a bouquet garni, and also left in a marinade for fish.

Old wives' tales say that bay stimulates the appetite, relieves pain, and is a remedy for skin and ear trouble. Wreaths of bay are often used as a symbol of success.

Bouquet garni

A bouquet garni is a little bunch of herbs tied together with thread, cooked with a casserole or stew, and removed before serving. Using the herbs in this way gives a subtle flavour to the dish without the flavour of the herbs being overwhelming.

The main ingredients of a bouquet garni are parsley stalks, bay leaf and a sprig of thyme, but other herbs can be added if liked, and marjoram is often one of the ingredients. Commercially prepared bouquets garnis are obtainable, either in little muslin bags or in little paper sacks just like teabags. However, at home it is very easy to prepare your own, using your own choice of herbs and tying them together in a square of muslin or thin cotton material. At the end of the cooking time the little bouquet garni must be removed from the casserole or stew and thrown away.

Chives

The history of chives goes back 5000 years to the days of the ancient Chinese, but its introduction to Great Britain was with the Romans.

Chives are easy to grow in any garden soil, and it's the hollow green grass which is used in the kitchen. To keep the grass green the flowers must be cut in the summer. Potted chives do well indoors and will give you a fresh supply of chives all year round.

The grass has a mild onion flavour and is usually eaten raw. The bright green colour is an attractive garnish for salads and vegetables, but the chives do need to be finely chopped with scissors first. A few of them mixed with mashed potatoes makes a world of difference.

Fennel

The flavour of fennel is very akin to liquorice and the herb should be used sparingly. It is quite easy to grow and the pretty green foliage is a delightful accompaniment to fish and a very attractive garnish on many other dishes.

The young stems of sweet fennel have a bulbous base and this can be sliced and eaten raw in salads. It is also very good sautéed – first slice the bulb, sauté in margarine and then cook slowly in the oven until soft. It takes about an hour.

I also like to use fennel sliced as a base on which to cook fish and you can find several recipes for its use in this book.

Garlic

Garlic is one of the strongest herbs used in the kitchen and should be added to dishes with great care. Dislike of garlic can often be traced back to a meal in which it figured too prominently.

Garlic is a hardy perennial, and can be grown in a sunny position in light, well-drained soil. The bulbs are dug up in late summer and then hung to dry in an airy place. Once dried, the bulbs are best kept in a cool dry place, but not airtight; a jam jar with holes in the lid makes an excellent container.

Garlic's strong lingering smell on the breath puts many people off, but if it is used with parsley in a recipe, the parsley removes the smell and leaves the flavour.

Garlic should be used sparingly. A cut clove rubbed around the inside of a salad bowl leaves just a slight hint of flavour, but when used in a recipe, the garlic should be well crushed, either in a garlic press or with the aid of the flat blade of a knife and a little salt. The salt acts as an abrasive and breaks down the fibres of the garlic.

Garlic contains volatile oil, so medicinally it is good for disorders of the digestion; it helps to keep down blood pressure, has antiseptic qualities and, when made into a cough mixture, is good for bronchitis. It can also be used in the treatment of gall bladder and liver troubles, headaches, fits, faintness, and skin blemishes. I suppose you could say that it is an all-round medicine.

Lemon balm

In a diet lacking in lemon juice, lemon balm is a useful herb to grow and use. It is a perennial and has light green heart-shaped leaves, wrinkled and veined. The yellowish-white flowers bloom all through the summer, but these should be cut off because only the leaves are needed in the kitchen.

Lemon balm has a lemon-scented flavour, and the leaves can be chopped and added to fish and poultry dishes and also sprinkled over salads and vegetables. As it is not too strong in flavour, it is a herb that can be used generously.

Medicinally, a tea made from the leaves helps to promote relaxation and good sleep.

Marjoram and oregano

There are three types of marjoram. Sweet marjoram, which is an annual, is the herb most preferred in the kitchen because it has the most delicate flavour. The second one, pot marjoram, is a perennial and has a rather less delicate flavour than the sweet one, but it grows vigorously and is an ideal pot plant. The third marjoram is also known as oregano. This is also a perennial, but grows in milder climates than ours. The flavour is much stronger than that of the other two and most oregano used is imported dried, often from Mediterranean regions.

Marjoram can be used fresh or dried but, when dried, less is needed to give the same amount of flavour as it is more concentrated.

To dry your own marjoram, the flowers and leaves should be cut on a dry day during the flowering period and then carefully hung up in a cool dark place; this way, the colour and flavour are best preserved.

Purchased dried marjoram and oregano are usually excellent, and both these herbs can be used in a variety of dishes. A little sprinkled in with TVP makes a very interesting addition and, as oregano comes from the Mediterranean, it is a perfect complement to aubergines and peppers. Vegetable soups also benefit from a pinch of the herb added whilst the soup is simmering.

Old wives' tales tell us that marjoram has antiseptic qualities, and an infusion can be made to take for the common cold and sore throats. It is also said that it helps to increase white corpuscles in the blood and to improve circulation.

Mint

Most gardens in England have a patch of mint, usually one of the three most common varieties, spearmint, applemint or peppermint, and they all have distinctive flavours and refreshing aromas.

Spearmint is the mint most usually used to provide the English with their traditional mint sauce to go with roast lamb, a sauce which has no place in this book. But any of the mints chopped and added to TVP mince give a most interesting combination.

Mint leaves added to new potatoes, peas and carrots during cooking impart a delicious flavour, and a little chopped mint sprinkled over salads is pleasant.

Old wives' tales abound about mint. It has a reputation as a tonic for indigestion; as a lotion it is said to be good for skin troubles, and fresh leaves rubbed on aching rheumatic joints are said to bring some relief.

Parsley

Parsley is one of the most common herbs and is used a great deal in the recipe section. A biennial with dark green curly leaves, it grows easily in most soils, and the dwarf curly variety is ideal for growing in a pot or window box, so that fresh parsley can be cut all year round.

Apart from the use of parsley as a garnish, it is a rich source of vitamin C, as well as containing protein, iodine, iron, calcium, magnesium and other trace minerals. Fresh parsley is by far the best sort to use, but if this is not always possible frozen parsley is the next best thing. Picking parsley encourages new growth, so it is best to pick it regularly and, if not needed, wash and shake dry and then freeze in a polythene bag. Dried parsley is a poor substitute, but it can be used if necessary.

Parsley can be used to flavour sauces and soups or added to salads, and can be sprinkled over vegetables as a garnish. The stalks can be used in a bouquet garni, and fried parsley is a delicious accompaniment to fried or grilled fish.

Old wives' tales often mention the use of parsley. A tea can be made which is an aid to digestion, cleans the kidneys, and is said to be beneficial to people with arthritis and rheumatism.

Rosemary

It is said that rosemary will only grow in the gardens of the righteous. Mind you, it likes light soils and a sunny position, and so if you cannot get it to grow in your garden it could well be the soil or position that is at fault rather than you. It is a delightful herb to have in the garden and it has many uses, culinary, medicinal and cosmetic.

The shrub has spiky green leaves and little blue or white flowers, it is the leaves which have so many uses.

Rosemary is best used when it is fresh, but it can be dried in late summer and the needles stripped from the twigs and used when needed. Commercially, dried leaves can be bought whole, or powdered, and the powdered rosemary is very useful for adding to a casserole when it would be difficult to remove the leaves from a finished dish. People who have rosemary growing in their gardens don't need to dry the leaves as they can be picked all the year round.

A sprig of rosemary placed inside a chicken before roasting imparts a delicious flavour. The flavour goes equally well with fish and vegetables, but as it is rather pungent, it is best to experiment to find out just how much you like to use. Powdered rosemary can be used in sweet cookery as well; a little added to a basic biscuit mixture makes a nice change.

Cosmetically, the infusion made from the leaves is a superb tonic for greasy hair, and helps many skin conditions. Medicinally, rosemary has a reputation for strengthening the brain and memory.

A large bush of rosemary is a joy in a garden, not only for the uses listed above, but also because it is very attractive. The foliage can even be used in flower arrangements, and these give out a delightful perfume in the summer.

Sage

Sage is a hardy perennial shrub which will grow in most soils. The leaves are rough and grey-green in colour, and the flavour is warm and slightly bitter, but very pungent. Sage leaves can be used fresh, either whole or chopped, and can also be used dry and crumbled. Sage takes a long time to dry and it is often better to buy dried sage rather than dry your own. Incorrectly dried sage has a very musty flavour and is not pleasant.

Sage, dried and made into a stuffing, goes well with chicken, or the whole fresh leaves can be cooked with the chicken. The fresh leaves can also be chopped and added to salads, or dipped whole in batter and deep-fried until golden-brown.

Bees love to visit the sage bush when in bloom, and sage honey is particularly delicious.

Medicinally, sage tea is a good tonic for the nerves and blood, and used as a mouthwash it helps to keep the teeth white.

Thyme

There are probably over 100 different varieties of thyme, but the one most frequently used is the common garden thyme. Lemon thyme is another fairly common variety which has a more delicate flavour.

Common garden thyme grows best in well-drained rock gardens but it can also be grown in indoor window boxes. Cutting encourages bushy growth and makes for an attractive plant.

The leaves can be used either fresh or dried and they have a slightly sharp flavour which is useful in a diet lacking in lemon juice and other acids.

Old wives' tales say that thyme aids digestion of rich foods, and a tea made from the leaves and sweetened with honey is an excellent cough mixture.

Spices

Cinnamon

True cinnamon comes from the bark of the cinnamon tree, which grows naturally in Sri Lanka and the Malabar coast of India, and commercially in the Seychelles and other eastern countries.

The fine, paper-thin bark is dried and as it dries it curls up into sticks. The dried bark can be finely ground into a powder and this ground cinnamon has a much stronger flavour than the bark, but it quickly loses its aroma. Because of this, ground cinnamon should only be purchased in very small quantities or, better still, a little of the bark should be ground in a pestle and mortar when needed. It is possible to buy other sweet aromatic barks, and one which is quite common in Great Britain is cassia. This bark is much thicker than the cinnamon and does not have such a fine flavour, but it can be used in the place of cinnamon bark and it is considerably cheaper than true cinnamon.

Powdered cinnamon has several uses, apart from its usual role as a spice added to biscuits and cakes. A little cinnamon sprinkled over cooked cabbage is delicious, or it can be mixed with sugar and then used as a topping for pancakes or honey dreams (recipe nos. 209 and 212).

Medicinally, cinnamon is astringent and, being antacid, it is helpful for stomach upsets and diarrhoea. It is also good for colds and sore throats.

Nutmeg and mace

Nutmeg trees grow on the islands of the East Indies, and both nutmeg and mace are imported in their dried form.

The fleshy fruit of the nutmeg tree is like an apricot and, when ripe, it splits to reveal the nutmeg kernel surrounded by a red net-like coating. This red coating is carefully stripped from around the kernel and then both this and the kernel are allowed to dry. During the drying process the red coating becomes brittle and changes colour from red to yellowish-brown. This is called mace. The mace and the dried kernel, which is called nutmeg, are imported into this country and sold either whole or ground.

Most people are familiar with nutmeg as a ground spice used in cakes or sprinkled over rice pudding, but the flavour of nutmeg goes well with white sauces made with soya milk. Also a little added to mashed potatoes makes a tremendous difference, and it can be sprinkled over other vegetables such as cauliflower and carrots.

Mace is not used so often and, although it comes from the same tree, it has quite a different flavour.

A small piece of mace placed with a piece of onion in a pan of warm soya milk and then left to infuse for 30 minutes will impart a delightful flavour. This milk can then be strained and used to make a white sauce to pour over vegetables, or it can be used to make a bread sauce. White fish baked in the oven in water or soya milk can be greatly improved by the addition of one piece or blade of mace. The resulting liquor can then be used to make a sauce to serve with the fish.

Medicinally, nutmeg aids digestion and is helpful against flatulence and vomiting, but it should always be used in small quantities as it can be very overpowering.

Vanilla

Vanilla, with its delicate, spicy and aromatic flavour, is widely used in cakes and biscuits and other sweet dishes. In a diet which shuns all chemical additives, purchased vanilla essence must also be shunned. Vanilla essence is produced by distilling oil of clove or by processing sucrose, waste paper or coal tar and this substitute vanilla has none of the true delicate flavour of the real thing and should have no place in our kitchen.

However, it is very simple to obtain true vanilla flavour because most health food shops sell vanilla pods. The pods should be placed in a jar and covered with sugar and then left for a week or so. Gradually the flavour of the vanilla will permeate the sugar, thus giving you natural flavour. The vanilla pods can be used over again, but they do lose their pungency after several months. They should be replaced as soon as you feel that the sugar is no longer taking up any flavour.

Conversion
Table

Conversion Table (with American Equivalents)

| | USA Cup Measures | | | |
	1 Cup	$\frac{1}{2}$ Cup	$\frac{1}{4}$ Cup	$\frac{1}{8}$ Cup
Almonds	125 g	75 g	40 g	20 g
	5 oz	3 oz	$1\frac{1}{2}$ oz	$\frac{3}{4}$ oz
Coconut	75 g	40 g	20 g	15 g
	3 oz	$1\frac{1}{2}$ oz	$\frac{3}{4}$ oz	$\frac{1}{2}$ oz
Flour	100 g	50 g	25 g	15 g
	4 oz	2 oz	1 oz	$\frac{1}{2}$ oz
Flour (Wholemeal)	115 g	65 g	25 g	15 g
	$4\frac{1}{2}$ oz	$2\frac{1}{4}$ oz	1 oz	$\frac{1}{2}$ oz
Fluids	250 ml	125 ml	75 ml	40 ml
	$\frac{1}{2}$ pt	$\frac{1}{4}$ pt	$\frac{1}{8}$ pt	$\frac{1}{16}$ pt
Macaroni	100 g	50 g	25 g	15 g
	4 oz	2 oz	1 oz	$\frac{1}{2}$ oz
Margarine	225 g	100 g	50 g	25 g
	8 oz	4 oz	2 oz	1 oz
Oatmeal	75 g	40 g	25 g	15 g
	3 oz	$1\frac{1}{2}$ oz	1 oz	$\frac{1}{2}$ oz
Peanuts	150 g	75 g	40 g	20 g
	5 oz	3 oz	$1\frac{1}{2}$ oz	$\frac{3}{4}$ oz
Peas	100 g	50 g	25 g	15 g
	4 oz	2 oz	1 oz	$\frac{1}{2}$ oz
Prawns	100 g	50 g	25 g	15 g
	4 oz	2 oz	1 oz	$\frac{1}{2}$ oz
Rice	200 g	100 g	50 g	25 g
	7 oz	4 oz	2 oz	1 oz
Soya flour	100 g	50 g	25 g	15 g
	4 oz	2 oz	$1\frac{1}{4}$ oz	$\frac{1}{2}$ oz

	USA Cup Measures			
	1 Cup	½ Cup	¼ Cup	⅛ Cup
Sugar (Brown)	200 g	100 g	50 g	25 g
	7 oz	4 oz	2 oz	1 oz
Sugar (Caster)	150 g	75 g	40 g	20 g
	5 oz	3 oz	1½ oz	¾ oz
Sugar (Icing)	115 g	60 g	33 g	15 g
	4½ oz	2¼ oz	1⅛ oz	½ oz
Walnuts	100 g	50 g	25 g	15 g
	4 oz	2 oz	1 oz	½ oz

As in the recipes, 25 g is taken as the equivalent of 1 oz.

Note: Because American cups are measurement by volume, commodities do not necessarily equate by weight.

Index